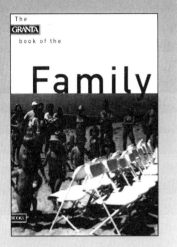

GRAND STREET

Space

54

Front cover: Jasper Johns, *Untitled* (detail), 1993.
Back cover: Vito Acconci, *Proposal for Klapper Hall,* 1993–1995.

Grand Street (ISSN 0734-5496; ISBN 1-885490-05-4) is published quarterly by Grand Street Press (a project of the New York Foundation for the Arts, Inc., a not-for-profit corporation), 131 Varick Street, Room 906, New York, NY 10013. Contributions and gifts to Grand Street Press are tax-deductible to the extent allowed by law. This publication is made possible, in part, by a grant from the National Endowment for the Arts.

Second-class postage paid at New York, NY and additional mailing offices. Postmaster: Please send address changes to Grand Street Subscription Service, Dept. GRS, P.O. Box 3000, Denville, NJ 07834. Subscriptions are $40 a year (four issues). Foreign subscriptions (including Canada) are $55 a year, payable in U.S. funds. Single-copy price is $12.95 ($15 in Canada). For subscription inquiries, please call (800) 807-6548.

Grand Street is printed by the Studley Press in Dalton, MA. It is distributed to the trade by D.A.P./Distributed Art Publishers, 636 Broadway, 12th floor, New York, NY 10012, Tel: (212) 473-5119, Fax: (212) 673-2887, and to newsstands only by B. DeBoer, Inc., 113 E. Centre Street, Nutley, NJ 07110 and Fine Print Distributors, 6448 Highway 290 E., Austin, TX 78723. *Grand Street* is distributed in Australia and New Zealand by Peribo Pty, Ltd., 58 Beaumont Road, Mount Kuring-Gai, NSW 2080, Tel: (2) 457-0011.

GRAND STREET

Editor
Jean Stein

Managing Editor
Deborah Treisman

Art Editor
Walter Hopps

Assistant Editor
Jackie McAllister

Designer
Jim Hinchee

Editorial Assistant
Julie A. Tate

Administrative Assistant
Lisa Brodus

Interns
Stephen F. Clark
Elisa Frohlich
John Henderson

Contributing Editors
Hilton Als, Dominique Bourgois, Colin de Land, Anne Doran,
Morgan Entrekin, Gary Fisketjon, Raymond Foye, Jonathan Galassi,
Stephen Graham, Barbara Heizer, Dennis Hopper, Hudson,
Andrew Kopkind (1935–1994), David Kornacker, Jane Kramer,
Erik Rieselbach, Edward W. Said, Robert Scheer, Elisabeth Sifton,
Jeremy Treglown, Katrina vanden Heuvel,
Gillian Walker, Drenka Willen

Publishers
Jean Stein & Torsten Wiesel

CONTENTS

Ghost of Chance

Captain Mission strapped on his double-barreled flintlock, which he kept loaded with shot charges, and thrust a scabbarded cutlass under his belt. He picked up his staff and walked out through the settlement, stopping here and there to talk to the settlers.

They found an excellent red clay for bricks and were constructing two-story dwellings with second-story balconies supported by heavy hardwood pillars. These buildings had been joined to form a tier, with the dining and kitchen areas in the two downstairs rooms and sleeping and dressing areas upstairs. The balconies were connected and were used for sleeping hammocks and pallets. These structures faced the sea, and steps led down to the bay, where a number of boats were moored.

•

The word for lemur meant 'ghost' in the native language. There were taboos against the killing of ghosts, and Mission had imposed an Article that prohibited killing them, on penalty of expulsion from the settlement. If any crime deserved the death penalty, also prohibited under the Articles, then this was that crime.

He was seeking a different lemur species, described by a native informant as much bigger—like a calf, or a little cow.

"Where are the big ghosts?"

The native gestured vaguely inland. "You must be careful of the evil Lizard-Who-Changes-Color. If you fall under its spell, you too will change color. You too will turn black with anger, and green with fear, and red with sex..."

"Well, what is so wrong with that?"

"In a year you will die. The colors will devour your skin and flesh."

"You were talking about a big ghost. Bigger than a goat... Where are they to be found?"

"When you hear Chebahaka, Man-in-the-Trees, then Big One not there. Her cannot be where noise is."

"Her?"

"Her. He. For Big Ghost is same."

"So. He is where Man-in-the-Trees isn't?"

"No. He is there when Man-in-the-Trees is silent."

This occurred at dawn and sunset.

•

Mission was heading inland, up a steep path that leveled off at five hundred feet above the sea. He stopped, leaning on his staff, and looked back. The steep climb had not touched his breath or brought sweat to his face. He saw the settlement, the freshly molded red bricks and thatch already timeless as houses in fairyland. He could see the shadows that lay under the pier, the lurking fish, the clear blue of the bay, the rocks and foliage, all floating in a limpid, frameless painting.

Silence descended like a shroud that would crumble to dust when he moved. Now a cat's-paw of wind frisked across the bay and up through the ferns and leaves, bringing to his face a breath of Panic. Little ghost paws rippled up his spine, stirring the hairs at the nape of his neck, where the death center flares briefly when a mortal dies.

Captain Mission did not fear Panic, the sudden, intolerable knowing that everything is alive. He was himself an emissary of Panic, of the knowledge that man fears above all else: the truth of his origin. It's so close. Just wipe away the words and look.

He moved through giant ferns and creepers in green shade without need of his cutlass, and stopped on the edge of a clearing. A moment of arrested motion, then a bush, a stone, a log moved, as a tribe of ring-tailed cat lemurs appeared, parading back and forth around each other, tails quivering above their heads. Then *whisk*—they were gone, drawing the space where they had been away with them. In the distance he could hear the cries of the sifaka lemur the natives called Chebahaka, Man-in-the-Trees.

With a quick motion he caught a grasshopper and knelt by a moss-covered log. A tiny face with round eyes and large trembling ears peered at him nervously. He held out the grasshopper, and the little mouse lemur fell upon it with chirping squeaks of delight, holding it in his small paws and nibbling quickly with his tiny needle teeth.

Mission moved toward the sound, which grew louder and louder. The Chebahakas saw him now, and they let out a concerted shriek that pierced his eardrums. Then suddenly the sound stopped, with an impact that threw him to the ground. He lay for some minutes in a half-faint, watching the gray shapes swing away through the trees.

Slowly he rose to his feet, leaning on his staff. Before him stood an ancient stone structure, overgrown with creepers and green with moss. He stepped through an archway, stone slabs under his feet. A large snake, of glistening bright green, glided down the steps leading to an underground room. Cautiously he descended. At the far end of the room an arch opened to admit the afternoon light, and he could see the stone walls and ceiling.

In the corner of the second room was an animal that looked like a small gorilla or chimpanzee. This surprised him, since he had been told that there were no true monkeys on the island. The creature was completely motionless, and black, as if formed out of darkness. He saw also a large pig creature of a light pink color, lolling on its side against the wall to his right.

Then, directly in front of him, he saw an animal that looked at first like a small deer. The animal came to his outstretched hand, and he saw that it had no horns. Its snout was long, and he glimpsed sharp teeth shaped like little scimitars. The long thin legs ended in cablelike fingers. The ears were large, flaring forward, the eyes limpid amber, in which the pupil floated like a glittering jewel, changing color with shifts of the light: obsidian, emerald, ruby, opal, amethyst, diamond.

Slowly the animal raised one paw and touched his face, stirring memories of the ancient betrayal. Tears streaming down his face, he stroked the animal's head. He knew he must get back to the settlement before dark. There is always something a man must do in time. For the deer ghost there was no time.

Faster and faster downhill, tearing his clothing on rocks and thorny vines, and by dusk he was back at the settlement. He knew at once that he was too late, that something was horribly wrong. No one would meet his eye. Then he saw Bradley Martin, standing over a dying lemur.

Mission could see that the lemur had been shot through the body. He felt a concentration of rage, like a red hot wave, but there was no reciprocal anger in Martin.

"Why?" Mission choked out.

"Stole my mango," Martin muttered insolently.

Mission's hand flew to the butt of his pistol.

Martin laughed. "You would violate your own Article, Captain?"

"No. But I will remind you of Article Twenty-Three: If two parties have a disagreement that cannot be settled, then the rule of the duel is applicable."

"Aye, but I do have the right to refuse your challenge, and I do."

Martin was an indifferent swordsman and a poor pistol shot.

"Then you must leave Libertatia, this very night, before the sun shall set. You have no more than an hour."

Without a word, Martin turned away and walked off in the direction of his dwelling. Mission covered the lemur with a tarpaulin, intending to take the body to the jungle and bury it the following morning.

In his quarters Mission was suddenly overcome by a paralyzing fatigue. He knew that he should follow Martin and settle the matter, but—as Martin had said—his own Articles... He lay down and fell immediately into a deep sleep. He dreamed there were dead lemurs scattered throughout the settlement, and woke up at dawn with tears streaming down his face.

Mission dressed and went out to get the dead lemur, but the lemur and the tarpaulin were both gone. With blinding clarity he understood why Martin had shot the lemur, and what he intended to do: he would go to the natives and say that the settlers were killing the lemurs and that, when he objected, they turned on him and he had barely escaped with his life. Lemurs were sacred to the natives in the area, and there was the danger of bloody reprisal.

Mission blamed himself bitterly for allowing Martin to escape. No use to go looking for him now. The damage was already done, and the natives would never believe Mission's denials.*

•

There are no further repercussions from the incident with Martin. But Mission does not slacken his precautions. He can feel Martin out there waiting his time with the cold reptilian patience of the perfect agent.

He had underestimated Martin from the beginning by not see-ing him. Martin had the capacity to create a lack of interest in himself.† Even his position was ambiguous, something between a petty officer and a member of the crew. But since there were no

---

* Consider the inexorable logic of the Big Lie. If a man has a consuming love for cats and dedicates himself to the protection of cats, you have only to accuse him of killing and mistreating cats. Your lie will have the unmistakable ring of truth, whereas his outraged denials will reek of falsehood and evasion.

Those who have heard voices from the nondominant brain hemisphere remark on the absolute authority of the voice. They know they are hearing the Truth. The fact that no evidence is adduced and that the voice may be talking utter nonsense is irrelevant. This is what the Truth *is*. And Truth has nothing to do with *facts*. Those who manipulate Truth to their advantage, the people of the Big Lie, are careful to shun facts. In fact nothing is more deeply offensive to such peo-ple than the concept of fact. To adduce fact in your defense is to rule yourself out of court.

In a prerecorded and therefore totally predictable universe, the blackest sin is to tamper with the prerecordings, which could result in altering the prere-corded future. Captain Mission was guilty of this sin. He threatened to demon-strate for all to see that three hundred souls can coexist in relative harmony with each other, with their neighbors, and with the ecosphere of flora and fauna.

† If you wish to conceal anything, you have only to create a lack of interest in the place where it is hidden.

petty officers, he occupied an empty space. And he made no attempt to fill it. When told to do something he did it quickly and efficiently. Yet he made no attempt to make himself useful.

Since Mission found contact with Martin vaguely disagreeable, he asked him to do less and less. Mission was displeased that Martin chose to join the settlers, but he did his share of the work and bothered no one. When he was not working he would simply sit, his face as empty as a plate. He was a large, sloppy man with a round pasty face and yellow hair. His eyes were dull and cold like lead.

Mission *saw* Martin for the first time as they confronted each other over the dying lemur. And what he saw inspired in him a deadly implacable hatred.

He sees Martin as the paid servant of everything he detests. No quarter, no compromise is possible. This is war to extermination.

•

Mission had smoked opium and hashish and had used a drug called *yage* by the Indians of South America. There must, he decided, be a special drug peculiar to this huge island, where there were so many creatures and plants not found anywhere else. After some inquiries he found that such a drug did exist: it was extracted from a parasitic fungus that grew only on a certain spiny plant found in the arid regions of the south.

The drug was called *indri*, which meant "look there" in the native language. For five gold florins he obtained a small supply from a friendly native. The drug was in the form of greenish-yellow crystals. The man, whose name was Babuchi, showed him exactly how much to take and cautioned him against taking more.

"Many take *indri* and see nothing different. Then they take more and see too much different."

"Is this a day or night drug?"

"Best at dawn and twilight."

Mission calculated an hour till sundown—enough time to reach his jungle camp.

"How long does it take to work?"

"Very quick."

Mission set out walking rapidly. Half an hour later, he took a small amount of the crystals with a sip of water from his goatskin water-bag. In a few minutes he experienced a shift of vision, as if his eyes were moving on separate pivots, and for the first time he saw Lizard-Who-Changes-Color. It was quite large, about two feet in length, and difficult to see, not because it took on the colors of its surroundings, but because it was absolutely motionless. He moved closer to the lizard, which brought one eye to bear on him and turned black with rage. Evidently Lizard-Who-Changes-Color did not like to be seen. Its colors subsided, to a neutral orange-yellow mottled with brown. And there was a gurkha lizard on a limb, as if carved from bark. It winked a golden eye at Mission.

Despite the need for vigilance, Mission was spending more and more time in the jungle with his lemurs. He had converted the ancient stone structure he had found into a dwelling. It was completely enveloped by the roots of a huge bulbous tree, as if held in a giant hand. The open arch in the second room was festooned with roots. There was a paved floor. He had covered the entrance with mosquito netting and arranged a pallet on the floor. Brushing the floor, he was surprised to find few insects, certainly no venomous varieties. The stone steps were worn smooth as if with the passage of many feet, perhaps not human feet.

Since his first encounter he had located a troop of large lemurs. These lemurs were too big and heavy to be comfortable in aboreal conditions and lived mostly on the land, in an area of grass and scrub where the forest thinned out, a mile from his campsite. Ideal grazing land, Mission realized with a shudder. The creatures were trusting and gentle and open to human affection.

Mission hurried on. He wanted to reach the ancient stone structure before twilight, and he hoped his special lemur would be there. He often slept with the lemur beside him on his pallet and had named the creature Ghost.

As Mission walked up, Ghost gave a little chittering cry of welcome. Mission took off his boots and hung his outer garment on wooden pegs driven into chinks in the stone wall. The only furniture was a wall-mounted table of rough-hewn planks supported on two legs, with an ink pot, quill pens, and parchment. In one corner were a small water keg with a spigot, some cooking utensils, an ax, a saw, hammers, a musket. Powder and shot were kept in the footlocker.

Mission sat at the wooden table beside his phantom, his Ghost, contemplating the mystery of the stone structure. Who could have built it?

Who?

He poses the question in hieroglyphs. . . a feather. . . He chooses a quill pen. Water. . . the clear water under the pier. A book. . . an old illustrated book with gilt edges. *The Ghost Lemurs of Madagascar.* Feather. . . a gull diving for garbage. . . the wakes of many ships in many places. A feather of Great Bird that lived here once, and the Sacred Lake two days' walk east, where every year a heifer is sacrificed to the Sacred Crocodile. Still, Mission wonders if there are other, similar structures on the island. . . .

Where?

A loaf of bread . . . water. . . a jar. . . a goose tied to a stake. Looking from one end of the island to the other, through the eyes of Lizard-Who-Changes-Color. Mission doesn't know why he is appalled by the questions that lunge into his mind, but he is satisfied, almost, to be appalled.

When?

A reed. . . a loaf of bread. . . A bird wheels in the sky. A woman plucks feathers from a fowl, takes a loaf of bread from an adobe oven. The split between the wild, the timeless, the free, and the tame, the time-bound, the tethered, like the tethered goose that will forever resent its bondage.

The structure that has already begun to obsess Mission could have been built at only one time, before the Split widened to a Chasm.

The concept of a question is reed and water. The question mark fades into reeds and water. The question does not exist.

Strange creatures are fitting stone together. Mission can't see them clearly, only their hands, like gray ropes. He senses the immense difficulty of an unaccustomed task. The stones are too heavy for these creatures' hands and bodies. Yet for some reason they must build this structure.

Why?

There is no reason why.

•

G host stirred beside Mission and belched a sweet scent of tamarind fruit. Despite Babuchi's warning, Captain Mission knew he must learn more.

He lit a candle and poured a reckless dose of *indri* crystals into his hand; he downed them with a cup of water. Almost immediately, he remembered the dream gorilla in the basement room, the strange pig creature he had seen, and then the gentle deer lemur.

Mission lay down by his Ghost. He wasn't sure he wanted to see what the *indri* would show him; already he knew that what he saw would be sad beyond endurance. He looked out through the tree roots as night sopped up the remaining light like a vast black sponge.

He lay there in the gray light, his arm around his lemur. The animal snuggled closer and put a paw up to his face. Tiny mouse lemurs stole out of the roots and niches and holes in the ancient tree and frisked around the room, falling on insects with little squeals. Their tails twitched above their heads; their great flaring ears, thin as paper, quivered to every sound as their wide limpid eyes swept the walls and floors for insects. They had been doing this for millions of years. The twitching tail, the trembling ears, mark the passage of centuries.

As the light drained into the sponge of the night, Mission could see for miles in every direction: the coastal rain forests, the mountains and scrub of the interior, the arid southern regions where the lemurs were frisking in the tall, spiny *Didierea* cactus. They gambol, leap, and whisk away into the remote past before the arrival of man on this island, before the beginning of time.

A n old picture book with gilt-edged etchings, onion paper over each picture... *The Ghost Lemurs of Madagascar* in gold script. Giant ferns and palms, bulbous tamarind trees, vines and bushes. In a corner of the picture is a huge bird, ten feet high, a plump, dowdy, helpless bird, obviously flightless. This bird tells one that here is a time pocket. There can be no predators in this forest, no large cats. In the middle of the picture is a ring-tailed lemur on a branch, looking straight out at the viewer. Now more lemurs appear, as in a puzzle....

The Lemur People are older than the Homo Sap, much older. They date back one hundred sixty million years, to the time when Madagascar split off from the mainland of Africa. Their way of think-ing and feeling is basically different from ours, not oriented toward time and sequence and causality. They find these concepts repugnant and difficult to understand.

One might think that a species that leaves no fossil record is gone forever, but Big Picture, the history of life on earth, is there for anyone to read. Mountain landmasses and jungles glide past, some slowing, some accelerating, vast rivers of land like saws splitting off islands, a great fissure, the landmasses rubbing against each other, then splitting, flying apart, faster and faster. . . slowing down to the great red island, with its deserts and rain forests, scrub mountains and lakes, its unique animals and plants, and the absence of predators or venomous reptiles, a vast sanctuary for the lemurs and for the delicate spirits that breathe through them, the glint in the jeweled eyes of a tree frog.

When attached to Africa, Madagascar was the ultimate landmass, sticking out like a disorderly tumor cut by a rift of future contours, this long rift like a vast indentation, like the cleft that divides the human body. The rift was miles across, and in others narrowed to a few hundred feet. It was an area of explosive change and contrast, swept by violent electrical storms, incredibly fertile in places, entirely barren in others.

The People of the Cleft, formulated chaos and accelerated time, flash through a hundred sixty million years to the Split. Which side are you on? Too late to change now. Separated by a curtain of fire. Like a vast festive ship launched with fireworks, the great red island moved majestically out to the sea, leaving a gaping wound in the earth's side, bleeding lava, and spurting noxious gases. It has lain moored in enchanted calm for a hundred and sixty million years.

Time is a human affliction; not a human invention but a prison. So what is the meaning of one hundred sixty million years without time? And what does time mean to foraging lemurs? No predators here, not much to fear. They have opposing thumbs but do not fashion tools; they have no need for tools. They are untouched by the evil that flows in and fills Homo Sap as he picks up a weapon—now *he* has the advantage. A terrible gloating feeling comes from knowing you've *got it!*

Beauty is always doomed. "The evil and armed draw near." Homo Sap with his weapons, his time, his insatiable greed, and ignorance so hideous it can never see its own face.

Man was born in time. He lives and dies in time. Wherever he goes, he takes time with him and imposes time.

Captain Mission was drifting out faster and faster, caught in a vast undertow of time. "Out and under, and out, and out," a voice repeated in his head.*

Mission knows the stone temple is the entrance to the biological Garden of Lost Chances. Pay and enter. He feels an impact of sadness that stops his breath, a catching, tearing grief. This grief can kill. He is beginning to learn the coinage here.

He remembers the pink pig creature, lost in passive weakness, slumped hopelessly against the wall, and the black simian against the far wall by the entrance, very still and very black, a blackness that glows. And the gentle deer lemur, extinct for two thousand years, the Ghost that shares his pallet. He moves forward through the roots that trail from the ancient stone arch. Somehow the black monkey creature is in front of him, and he looks into its eyes, completely black. It is singing a black song, a harsh melody of a blackness too pure to survive in time. It is only compromise that survives; that is why Homo Sap is such a muddled, unsightly creature, precariously and hysterically defending a position that he knows is hopelessly compromised.

Mission moves through a black tunnel, which opens to a series of dioramas: the last deer lemur falls to a hunter's arrow. Passenger pigeons rain from the trees to salvos of gunfire and plump down on the plates of fat bankers and politicians with their gold watch chains and gold fillings. The humans belch out the last passenger pigeon. The last Tasmanian wolf limps through a blue twilight, one leg shattered by a hunter's bullet. As do the almosts, the might-have-beens who had one chance in a billion and lost.†

Observe the observer observed.

---

* Erase the concept of a question from your mind. The Egyptian glyph is a reed or feather and water. Who? The water the feather the book. Wipe it out with the squawking goose of where and the bread of when, fading into a great, extinct flightless bird in a swampy pool.

† When we see the planet as an organism, it is obvious who the enemies of the planet are. Their name is legion. They dominate and populate the planet. "The deceived and the deceivers who see themselves as deceived." Did Homo Sap think other animals were there just for him to *eat*? Apparently. Bulldozers are destroying rain forests, the cowering lemurs and flying foxes, the singing Kloss's gibbons, which produce the most beautiful and variegated music of any land animal, and the gliding colugo lemurs, which are helpless on the ground. All going, to make way for more and more devalued human stock, with less and less wild spark, the priceless ingredient—energy into matter. A vast mud slide of soulless sludge.

So You Won't Be a Witness Today Either

Anything, even an exhausted wink,
  a look askance,
    a careless side-glance at the clouds, the lilacs,
is enough for you not to be a witness today, too,
not to see the indifferent bullets soaring through
your room,
the green stable of worms near your woman's face,
not to see yourself in another,
nor in yourself, either;
a little eye-tango in the blue,
a shred dance of the pupil is enough
to make gardens,
    gables,
      roofs tilt,
        tiles redly tremble,
to make you see the skin of ancient mummies also quivering
as though they were living,
as though light were rushing all about them,
haranguing you even from the glass coffins,
you, who can't tell for yourself: are these
  voices you hear,
is your hand,
  this wind,
    this summer with the trembling of long trees
  all just in your memory
or have you grown to be the earth's souvenir, perishing,
a muddled body among the timbers, in weeds,
and here in the site of your heart
there's only your left side, aching—

May the Water Keep Vigil with Me

I wake. Outside there's a lake
and a foreign country's darkness.
Inscrutable cry of bird
under the bushes,
as though someone were being murdered.

My head's heavy with drinking,
heavy with myself. In my recent dream
shirtless soldiers were running
and combing the ruffled park
with raised pitchforks.

Were they looking for me? For you, the long-banished?
I can't remember anymore. A bloodstain
shone darkly on a stone. Past that, a storm lantern,
overturned. The flame mingled with the mud
and made everything so finite, so shameless.

I'd like to sleep for spite, too. I'd like to forget
my European dream, the horror of those flat on their backs,
but in this foreign silence I'm just stumbling and groping;
I turn on the tap, let the water flow,
may it keep vigil with me till morning.

Translated from the Hungarian by
Len Roberts and Anette Marta

Parks, Streets, and Vehicles

P ublic space is made, not born. What is called "public space" in a city is produced by a government agency (in the form of a park) or by a private corporation (in the form of an office building's plaza or atrium). What is produced is a "product": it's bartered, by the corporation, in exchange for the right to build their building higher. It's granted, by the government agency, as a public benefit, as part of a welfare system. What's produced is a "production": a spectacle that glorifies the corporation or the state, or the two working together (the two having worked together in the back room, behind the scenes, with compromises and payoffs). The space, then, is *loaned* to the public, *bestowed* on the public. Public space is a contract between big and small, parent and child, institution and individual. Public space belongs to them and they in turn belong to the state.

•

Milling in the crowd, lost in the crowd, are the "others"—the outsiders, the people who have broken the contract, the people who don't have a home here. Public space doesn't belong to them. For them, it has to be taken. It is not a contract, but a strategy. *If we take the space, we can only hold it for a while, until the police come.*

•

A public space, on a city plan, is an in-between place, or an out-of-the-way place, a transition between home and workplace, or on the margins of home or workplace. The public space is between the intimacy of home and the aggression of work, between love and war. A public space is a civic space, and a civilized place. Each person, having the right to be there, has the responsibility to respect other people's rights. No person owns a place within the public space: it is a conglomerate of private spaces, temporary *(cont'd on p. 33)*

Personal Island, Floriade, Zoetemeer, The Netherlands, 1992.
A rowboat, wedged into a circular plane of grass, which can pull out of a semi-circular cut in the shore and head out to sea. (Foreground): Another boat is filled with soil, grass, and a growing tree; the oars are embedded in the ground.

Mobile Linear City, 1991.
A city packed into storage: six housing units, sheathed in corrugated steel, are telescoped into one semi-trailer hooked up to a tractor that travels as a conventional truck.

With Steven Holl:
Project for Storefront (Wall Machine), 1993. Storefront for Art and Architecture, New York. The facade wall of a gallery for architecture and art was divided with horizontal and vertical seams into pivoting panels that could adjust variously for different exhibition needs.

Project for Klapper Hall, Queens College, New York, 1993–1995.
On a college campus, the plaza in front of the English Department building becomes a field of spheres,
cut and formed to make passages, to provide seating, and to dispense lighting.

Project for Tachikawa City (Car/Sidewalk/Seat), Japan, 1994.
A car made of the same granite as the sidewalk is split in half lengthwise to function as
a bench and a bollard.

Above and overleaf: *Project for South Gateway,* Dayton, Ohio, 1994.
In the middle of Main Street, a few blocks away from the Civil War monument at the North Gateway, a traffic island becomes a celebration of powered flight.

(cont'd from p. 24) residences. You can keep your place, as long as you keep *to* your place. You can't move your place with you. You can encounter another person and share the place, but you can't move the other person's body out of the way, nor can your body blend with that body—you can, for example, (if the other person lets you) touch, or kiss, or hug, but you'd better not fuck (at least not where others can see you). The public space is pre-space: an occasion for introductions, temptations, planning for the future.

•

A public space is occupied by private bodies. These private bodies have hidden feelings, lives, and dreams. Underneath the manners, underneath the civilities, underneath the appearances, underneath the clothes, is a seething mass of anger and desire. The wonder of the city is: with all these bodies crowded next to each other, why aren't they all tearing each other's clothes off? The wonder of the city is: with all these bodies blocking each other, why aren't they all tearing each other apart limb from limb? Public space is the last gasp of the civilized world; public space is the Great White Hope; public space is belief and religion; public space is wishful thinking.

•

A space that's usable by people becomes, in the end, used, and used up. The ultimate public space is a ravaged space: the space has been used so much by people that the space is used up, it disintegrates under their feet.

—Vito Acconci

Time Channel

We have a television channel that forecasts hours and minutes. The host wears black, like an undertaker, and points at a huge clock with a stick. We watch the future change into the past before our eyes. How boring, you must think. I admit there is a certain monotony, a certain lulling indolence. Some people watch this channel because at least there won't be any surprises. Others, like myself, dream of the impossible: the demon of chance with his finger in the gears of the clock, minutes, hours, mislaid.

The host explains that if we pay close attention, we'll see the long hand of the clock move. It's true. It twitches. You might even say it has a nervous tick. The short hand, however, appears stuck and that's why I watch. In exactly sixty minutes, the host predicts, the short hand will have moved to the next number. My eyes don't leave the clock. I blink and blink and see nothing. The short hand has now reached two, and the host confirms the fact in a voice tinged with triumph.

There is also a thin, quick-moving hand that indicates seconds. It moves so quickly that, by the time you ask yourself where it is, it is somewhere else. Time is everywhere and yet nowhere. Every now is already a when.

The evening host wears a striped suit, an Elvis Presley wig, and a big smile. He claps his hands, announcing happily: "Here comes eleven o'clock." He scratches his head and says: "If nothing were to pass away, there would be no time." Or, just before a commercial: "In Paris, the night is already over while, in San Francisco, the dusk is just falling."

The commercials peddle the usual stuff: potato chips, Caribbean cruises, used cars at incredibly low prices. The more uncommon items are a board game called Zeno's Paradox and a California wine—one sip of which can supposedly change the direction of time.

At midnight a dark-haired lady comes to serve as a host. Her name is Lana Malone. She wears a tight red dress to accentuate her hourglass figure. She speaks in hoarse whispers as if confiding a great secret. It's ten to four, she says, and your heart skips a beat. My friend Freddie who is an even greater insomniac than I am, and who stays up all night checking the accuracy of his watch, heard her say one night between official announcements: "When you kiss me, sweetheart, the world stops turning."

Time exists only where counting exists and counting is an activity of a lonely soul. So, turn on your television set and flick past the channel of the gypsy fortune tellers, past the channel devoted to insane asylum inmates, past the channel that shows reruns of old state executions, to the channel that tells the time.

Delirium

The gesture toward height: every first-year student of architecture learns, with awe, that it was Ariel Price who made the city tall. Certainly in the history of the skyscraper there are earlier bold innovations, later twists and refinements, but the theoretical thrust—the celebration of tallness itself as an instrument of urban density and verticality as the primary orientation of urban flow—this can be ascribed only to the genius of the early Price.

A gesture perhaps less marked, because less visible, is to my mind more important, however, in the understanding of the way that Price's work grows inextricably from life: the gesture toward depth. It was Ariel Price who first banished the urban mall to the dark places beneath the street.

Some have argued that the creation of the sub-city is simply a means of cleaning up the landscape, of clearing the ground plane for the placement of crystalline lobbies against the emptiness of plaza and street, but it is more. It is the recognition of a new cosmological picture. It is the celebration of Romantic Nature. It is the elevation of Hell over Heaven. It is, in other words, a revolution.

It was on a cold September day, in the early stages of Mr. Price's sojourn in the forsaken city of Toronto, that he first looked out into the gray plaza to see a young girl dancing in front of a paper cup filled with coins...

•

The distinguished Ariel Price had rented an office on the second floor of the Letztesman Tower. He was not pleased with the level of his office. The second floor should not by rights exist in a Pricean tower, except as a cathedral ceiling in the expanse of the lobby. But this was an unambitious building, sketched by a famous Toronto modernist whose sole claim to prominence seemed to be the inclusion of pieces of Precambrian Shield in loose mosaic patterns on the walls.

International Regionalism: Ariel had winced when he heard this. Why not Cosmopolitan Provincialism? After a few weeks in Canada he grew accustomed to the spirit of the place: nonsense and compromise. This was a country with a Progressive Conservative party.

The Letztesman Tower had a small plaza appended to the west wall, a designated public space, which for some reason the public avoided assiduously. In winter, the winds would blow great drifts of snow up against one edge of the space and swirl eddies of loose powder over the sludge in the middle; in the spring, the plaza would be abandoned in favor of the tiny urban parkettes; and in summer, it would bake and crack beneath an intolerable sun. Now, at the onset of fall, inadequate drainage had made most of the plaza into an inch-deep pool, stagnant and filthy with leaves. Why the young girl had chosen this, the Letztesman Plaza, as a performance space, Ariel Price could not determine. It was simultaneously heartbreaking and enchanting, the guileless choice of this sad deserted theater. Ariel knew from watching that none of the coins in the soggy cup were thrown there by ardent admirers; he was as far as he could tell the only ardent admirer; he had seen the girl empty a cloth purse into the cup before beginning her desperately cheerful routine.

The act of watching, surreptitious watching, breeds an approximation of love. Ariel Price watched the girl through the one-way mirror of his office window, himself unwatched, and something stirred in his grand reptilian heart. And here, dancing in the cold perfect eye of a lizard, young Evelyn revealed to heightened advantage all of the subtle ordinary human traits which made her capable of being loved. Her face was pretty but irregular. Her complexion was still youthful, clear and almost unreal in coloration, but beginning to give way to the effects of a hard life: desperate lines around the mouth and eyes, an all-too-white substratum on which the colors of exertion read like fever. And her eyes, tremulous and vulnerable to a fault. They took you in, those eyes, were an invitation to great and dangerous intimacy. They illuminated, without softening, the terrible nakedness of the inner life. She danced poorly.

Ariel Price, coldly professional in even the most creative act, was, for the first time in his life, utterly charmed.

•

There is a voice from the stones. A soft voice, no more substantial than the soft halo that rings the streetlamps on a humid night. You've heard it. Alone at night, walking the downtown streets, you've stood in the steam from a grating and heard this voice.

Home was far to the north, but she had left that place and come down here to Toronto, not because she expected to be happy but simply to leave behind the shame. She made her way down with the trucks.

Evelyn knew about the truck routes; her father had driven a semi. She knew that the drivers would pull into truck stops at regular intervals to eat or sleep, and she made these her points of encounter. She would fall asleep at a table with a cardboard sign propped beside her: "Take me to Toronto. Please?"

It was the question mark which set her apart. In past years the roads had been clogged with dreaming youth, filthy and wide-eyed and far too thin, and over the course of time the truckers had grown wary. These children did not respect the simple courtesies of the road. There were laws between strangers, and for years these had held true, but they were based on the unwritten principle of reciprocity: if you bought a man his dinner as he hitched across the country, it was not so much out of simple generosity as it was in hope that someone might do the same for you should life change. These children understood nothing of this. They simply took, and then took more, and expected that the world would continue to give. By the time Evelyn made her way to Toronto, the truckers had grown cynical.

Please? The word itself was rare enough, the pleading question mark almost forgotten: it suggested not only youth but vulnerability, need made soft by weakness. Though most had given up on traveling children, every man at his coffee still felt a peculiar debt to Evelyn. Her kind. Every man had left someone, if not permanently then at least for too long, and leaving puts this accusation in its wake: you have left me, and I may not survive without you. In helping Evelyn survive the long journey south, every trucker was paying a small piece of this debt.

Toronto had seemed to her the most sophisticated, the most dangerous place on earth. The shame of a teenage girl from the North was nothing beside the torment and stress of every moment in this city. Here was the great pattern of life. Here she was small.

Her last ride was in a pickup truck, which took her down Yonge Street as the sun rose. The gathering together of the city was so fast and terrible, coming from nothing, gas stations and roadside patches of settlement angry as weeds, giving way to the tall and instantly bleak pretension of the suburb. Before he left, her father had taken her on modest excursions, and she would wake after midnight, wrapped in cotton flannel and sleepy, to find strange light caught in the cracks of the windshield: the light of northern cities, Sault Ste. Marie, Thunder Bay. Even these were more than her quiet mind could fathom, and she would close her eyes and curl back into the cracked leather seat.

The first day she spent simply wandering between the tallness of the buildings, taking it all in. There were objects made by man that dwarfed even trees; of course she had known this, but to see it, to be made small herself by these creations, was new and struck her with sickness and awe.

After her father had disappeared, she had slept with most of the boys in town, and it had seemed a fine thing at the time, all that attention, but they began to talk about her, to expect things, and she had to find another place. The last night in her town up north, they had taken her, every one of them in order. Later she would remember the garage in which it happened as if it were not quite real, a dark object, a built shadow. It shone, if that were the word, with negative light, swallowing memories. It became a church for her. A temple of shame. Always, when she tried to remember home, she would orient herself toward that dark garage as if in prayer, and her memories would go black like a spreading bruise.

Of all the boys who had fucked her in succession in that garage, only one was as thin and pale as she was, and Evelyn knew that he hated himself for being among them. For months she had kept herself from him, sneering, until this night, and she had watched his eyes grow painful with obsession like the shadows in winter, and she knew that he had entered her on that night with something deeper and more violent than love: it was retribution, because she had made him feel insignificant, nothing. She could not go back for two reasons: there was the group, and the snickering hatred that bound them against her; and there was this boy, Peter, whom she now remembered with growing regret. Evelyn had given herself to him in a way that would cast them apart forever. She had never wanted him, but now she was both his and not his in a way that made her terribly sad, and she knew that he suffered even more.

Before her father left, of course, Evelyn had never slept with any boy. His presence prevented it and the very idea of it: the act was neither permissible nor necessary. But she was thirteen when he left, and a new wilderness had grown within her, the soul, once childish and orderly, gone tortuous like the map of a strange continent. She needed more and darker things than the world could give. Evelyn discovered that she could want conflicting objects at the same time: comfort and humiliation, closeness and distance, silence and crying. More than once she had found herself naked with boys from the town whose ordinary selves had been wrenched out of shape by the contradictory nature of her desires, her loathing, her need. She brought out the vulgar side of sweet boys, made the brutal ones cry, and both grew to despise her way of making them over into cripples and demons. She found nothing, of course, in her feverish promiscuity but further distance from a father far away.

Evelyn hoped that the city might harden her as this abuse never had: she had become increasingly weak and open and trusting, with every boy who pushed his fingers up her to make her cry with pain. Sometimes it occurred to her that she wanted one boy, just one, to cause her the pain that her father had caused by leaving, but nobody could. Perhaps Toronto would harden her against this. She wanted to be tough, like the whores who came up from the Sault, drunk and icy and a little bit dead.

On Yonge Street, later, she met an entire community of these, some of them younger than she was, and it occurred to her that she had been wrong. She did not want to become hard. She wanted to become so weak that the world would tear its eyes out and weep blood for her pain; so kind and soft that every vicious boy would expire with grief; so lovely in her weakness that Peter would be transformed into a man and would forgive himself, and her, and would take her to meet her father so that she could touch his forehead and forgive him too.

•

A riel Price had come from Berlin at the invitation of the municipal government to design and build the tallest and most elegant tower in the country. He already knew what form the tower itself would take, but he had not yet solved crucial problems at the street level: how would the building address the ground plane, the Letztesman Plaza, the pedestrian alleys? Circulation was everything, and he wanted to get it right.

His office looked out over the proposed site, and Ariel would sit there for hours, staring at the fenced lot and wondering what he could do to enhance the placement of the lobby. Lately, the daily appearance of Evelyn in the plaza had derailed his serious contemplation. It was difficult to concentrate upon matters of linear and material perfection with this imperfect gypsy performing her graceless dance in his line of vision. *Damn her to hell.*

It was, in a sense, irresponsible to permit the foundations to be dug before he had resolved crucial details of the tower in his mind, but his reputation was such that he was not to be questioned, and it was something of a game with him to put himself in this kind of position: a theoretical labyrinth from which he could extricate himself only by way of a concentrated, virtuoso performance. It was a test of the nerves and a proof of the artist.

Ariel's assistant, Cosimo, stood at his shoulder as he watched the girl dance. "She's not very good, is she. Pretty, in a way, but not very good . . . "

"Shut up." This bloody assistant, assigned to him without consultation, made him twitch. The boy could draw, certainly, and he had ideas, but he was physically deformed. First in his class at the University of Toronto School of Architecture—all very well—but one arm was longer than the other, he limped, and his face was villainous. His hairline receded irregularly as a result of a massive birthmark over the scalp, and everything conspired to abort symmetry: one eye was lower than the other, one nostril larger, one shoulder pressed against his neck as if he were trying to hold a telephone while typing. *Who are you to cast judgment on the physique of this girl?* He wanted to say this, but did not. The boy was useful.

Cosimo flinched and was silent. He had known in advance that Mr. Price would be a difficult and demanding master, less polite than his Canadian teachers; Cosimo had been raised by an extended family of Calabrian builders, and he was accustomed to rough treatment on the work site. What he could not yet understand, however, was how the brusque manner of the great architect did not seem to conceal any real desire to teach. When his father had berated him for clumsiness, it had been understood that Cosimo was being prepared for the world: that the treatment, however painful, was motivated by affection and care. Cosimo had no doubt that Ariel Price, a legendary architect, would possess a far greater depth of humanity than a rough construction worker one generation removed from a small Italian village, but he had yet to discover any sign of it.

Still, he was cautious around the great man, and when Ariel told him to shut up—however inappropriately and without apparent motive—he shut up. The girl dancing in the square was a poor dancer; nothing Ariel Price could say would alter that fact; but similarly, nothing Cosimo could say would add anything to the truth of it. Beauty was beauty, and required neither justification nor championship: it just was.

•

The beds in the hostel were pushed together to fit as many as possible into the room, with no space to walk between them. Evelyn had never spent a night with this many girls. It was different, somehow, from her night with all the boys in the garage: she felt strangely shy around these women in a way that she never had with boys. They spoke differently, and had customs learned on the streets of the city that made her nervous and tongue-tied. Evelyn remained silent and listened and, when it came time to go to bed, she made her way anxiously down the row of beds and crawled over the foot of the one assigned to her. The lights were still on. She felt exposed, and pulled the sheet over her head. Her eyes were open in this tent of white, so that when the girl next to her reached over to put her hand on Evelyn's shoulder, she could see the shadow approaching.

"Hey."

Evelyn emerged carefully from beneath the sheet to find an older girl, perhaps eighteen, eyeing her with curiosity.

"First night?"

Evelyn nodded.

At night conversation takes invisible wings. The darkness of the hour, the crisp sound of the voice in the midst of silence: these call messengers down. The solitary air denies itself. In the vast and empty quiet, listening begins. A night of such conversation, especially when combined with the terrible loneliness of youth, the urgent need which attaches to all things, can forge strong bonds of friendship with almost pathological haste.

On this night, Evelyn heard for the first time a story that would alter the course of her self. Aimee told her, in pious detail and with great inaccuracy, the story of a woman who seemed to offer hope to even them, the whore who became mysterious and holy even among the saints: she told her, as she had heard it whispered on the streets of Toronto, the story of Mary Magdalene.

"Once there was a girl, like me, who fucked men for money. You're going to do it some day, now that you're here: you're going to do it for money, it's not so terrible—well, it is—but anyway, let me tell you about this girl.

"She sits in a window. They don't have glass like us: they use big sheets of salt, which they find by the side of the sea, and you can see through them. She's looking through this pane of salt. Before she looks, she puts on her lipstick. And just before that, she's been doing it, you know, with this Roman soldier, and she's not wearing anything, and she sits on this bench next to the window and looks out.

"And this place she lives in, it's a big city, and she lives in this suburb just beside the sea. And her name is Mary. Mary Mary. Twice, like that: they call her Mary Mary. And then when she gets to be a saint they call her Saints Mary, 'cause there's two of her. The first part of her is a slut like me, and the second part of her—

the second Mary—is the girl who looks out the window and gets changed into the most holy and best person, like you've never met before in your whole life.

"And everybody who's ever changed or wanted to change prays to her."

Aimee wriggled out from under the sheets, paused for a moment, then shifted awkwardly across to Evelyn's bed, who made room. They stared at each other. She slipped under the sheets with Evelyn.

"You don't mind?"

Evelyn shook her head. Aimee held Evelyn's hand, lightly, and started the story from the beginning.

"Now this girl we're talking about grew up pretty normal and nice, except she didn't have a father. Her family was a good family and she was a pretty good kid, you know. She worked for her mom at this cafeteria on the main street, called Knight and Day, which is a stupid joke, but it was open all night and it had a picture of this knight in shining armor on the sign. Mary Mary used to flip the saltburgers and act cute to the customers, who liked her, and she went to school and stuff and was all set to have a normal life when something really terrible happened.

"She was doing the late-night shift, which she was allowed to do on weekends, and this traveling snake-oil rat-shit con man was in one of the booths trying to sell some stuff, and when he saw Mary Mary he called her over and put his arm around her and said to the guy he was talking to: this here's the little slut who used to belong to that yellow pigeon we had bashed in down Rome way. You don't remember this, sweetheart—and here he gave Mary Mary a little tweak with his finger—but your daddy was the yellowest little shit stain this side of Jerusalem, and because of him I did six years in the salt mines, and because of his big mouth we had the Man put his head in a vise, like this, right? And crush it, slowly, so his brains came out his ears.

"And that's when the family of Mary Mary started having their first problem with demons."

•

A fter a fortnight of watching, during which the tower pro-
gressed so slowly that the clients were beginning to have
reservations about the great man, Ariel decided to take his
lunch into the square. The girl was dancing, as always. Ariel sat
rigidly on a slim concrete bench directly in front of the girl, who
hopped nervously from one foot to the other and did her best not
to meet his eyes. He smiled an agitated smile that tried to look
satisfied and patronizing, but increasingly resembled a predatory
leer. He tore at his sandwich with his teeth.

For a man almost sixty, Ariel had an uncommonly youthful face.
His hair had been white from his mid-twenties, at which time he
seemed strangely old for his years, but he had not visibly aged much
since then, and could still pass for a man of perhaps thirty or forty.
And he had *gravitas*, a very European attribute, an ancient way of
carrying himself which seemed faintly ludicrous in North America—
he looked as if he ought to be wearing a toga. All of this combined
to unnerve the poor dancing girl almost completely.

He smiled as he chewed his turkey.

Cosimo, who was surprised to find Ariel Price absent from the
office—the great man insisted upon the entire staff taking lunch at
their desks—glanced out the window and discovered, with a shock
of mixed emotions, Herr Price on his bench and the young girl,
dancing in his vision, impaled there like a fish squirming on a spear.

From the ideal vantage point, suspended above the square, the
lines of sight come together like vectors, lines of desire with force
and direction: Ariel, Evelyn, Cosimo.

When the architect stood to place a penny in the cup, the girl
stopped dancing, grabbed the cup, and prepared to dart from the
plaza. Ariel held out his penny and smiled. Evelyn cringed and froze,
a deer in a headlight, her face twisted with revulsion. Ariel ceased
to smile, and Cosimo turned pale.

The pattern of forces shines with a new and mysterious ten-
dency. It burns like the light through a crystal, focused and geo-
metrically profound, the simple pattern coheres hard and bright
and eternal and becomes the inevitable seed, the acorn at the core,
the beginning of the ineluctable course of events: the dread narrative. This is the genesis of plot. The story will grow outward in rings.

Without waiting for her penny, Evelyn ran. Ariel stood. Cosimo
saw the expression on the architect's face and shivered: slowly, and

with great malice, the great man smiled.

Ariel Price had resolved in his mind the problem of the mall.

•

The kind of demon Mary Mary got first was a young girl demon: it's like this thing that drives you to take everything you want and ruin it from wanting. And, what's weird is, the thing she wanted was Roman soldiers. Or maybe I should say love, because that's the thing she really wanted, but that got changed pretty quickly, you know, ruined through too much wanting, until what she thought she wanted was more and more men, and the ones who were always there and moving through town and getting replaced were soldiers.

We're talking now about a girl who's, like, fourteen, and she's putting on makeup and taking the train to Rome on a regular basis, and dancing for these seriously evil men, who poke her with weapons, and laugh at her, and then fuck her when they're finished.

And one time too many she gets thrown out into the street when they're finished and finds herself hungry, and fighting the gutter dogs for a piece of salt, and that's when she decides—and let's face it, the demon helps make these decisions for you—that's when she decides that she isn't going to give it away anymore. You want me, thinks Mary Mary, you want to watch me dance, and make fun of me, and fuck me when you please, you're going to have to pay for it.

So now, when she finds herself in the Roman streets, after a night with the soldiers, she's got all their money in her pockets. And they treat her better; they don't just kick her out; they walk her right to the door and say goodbye, because she's rich with their money, and now they have to respect her. But no one really respects her. Men want her, and they hate her, but the wanting weighs even more than the hate, so they don't kill her, and—you know something interesting?—they pay her twice: once by coming into her and going all limp and weak, and once with cash, which they've worked for and have to give to her instead of their wives or whoever deserves it. And when she leaves, they're even more sad than she is.

So, from being a girl from nowhere, she becomes this strong and really desirable woman in the biggest city of them all, and you could even maybe call her successful, in a way, except that she's a whore, and weirdly, you know, even in the eyes of these assholes who pay and admire her, she's just about the lowest piece of scum in the world, like something they might find on their sandal after walking through a filthy street, and yeah they love her but they also hate her and that's how it always is, you know: she lies naked for them, all naked and serene, all wrapped up in their love and admiration, just this side of getting the shit kicked out of her.

•

T he labyrinth is an image of the city. And the city itself is an image of the human mind. The mind is always looking to expand its hegemony: this is the drive toward architecture. After torturing its own substance into a semblance of submission through the device of reason, the mind turns outward; and the natural sphere of colonization is the realm immediately in front of the bright, acquisitive eyes: the domain of the real.

In forcing the real to conform to rules—in building cities—the mind naturally chooses a familiar form. The city takes, inevitably, the shape of the mind itself. But the mind does not know its own shape. And the part of the soul that is dark finds its way into the real by a process of duplication: the city breeds another city, infernal and unknown to the light, a dark mirror.

When the queen fornicates with the bull from the sea, and gives birth to a monster, the king—whose own arrogance moved him to keep the sacred bull that was not his—decides to banish the loathsome offspring to a place beneath the city, a dark place that looks for all the world like a tangle of streets, except that there is no map and only one exit. And the architect—whose arrogance moved him to create the device whereby the queen violated nature and took the great bull between her white legs—turns his genius toward the creation of the labyrinth.

When Ariel Price finds that the city of Toronto offers no place for the proper expansion of his lust for the dancing girl, he proposes to build an underground mall. And the mall becomes the type of itself: the sub-city, the sewer, the catacomb, the grave.

•

47

osimo carried himself across the Letztesman Plaza, feeling in his skin the unliving concrete around him, florid with dying light, and then he sensed—as one does—another creature, close by, sentient and perceptive: a mind with a world of its own, sharing the dead space with his shameful body.

Lying beneath the stone bench, and shivering with hunger, was the frail form of a young dancing girl.

The girl felt his touch, and opened her eyes, then closed them with revulsion. *Is my weakness merely this: an invitation to monsters?* But there was something in the texture of his skin that was different: it seemed horribly open to sensation, careful and alive, as if it were capable of judging the difference between fine and less fine paper— and of course it was—and Evelyn opened her eyes again to meet the eyes of the bent student who had touched her.

"Are you cold?"

The girl nodded, closing her eyes again.

"Hungry?"

She continued to nod.

"Come with me. We'll get something to eat."

The eyes opened, a little wet now, like sexual organs. "I just want something small. Something small. Not expensive. Okay?"

"Sure. We'll get soup and bread and pasta, it's cheap. Come with me."

The girl stood, swaying slightly, and Cosimo made to catch her should she sicken and fall, but she did not. She clung to his arm with one strong hand, and he felt new strength radiating from the bruise that she made: she will hurt me with need, this girl. They walked together, Cosimo with great care, and Evelyn with deliberate but faltering steps, and for the first time in his life Cosimo was not the cripple.

He took her up the stairs to his second-floor apartment and left her sprawled on his mattress as he shopped for food. He returned quickly, almost running, because it seemed impossible to him that she would not disappear in his absence. Some things were not meant to be, and a woman laid out upon his mattress in an attitude of sex, or perhaps death or prayer, was not part of what was meant to be. The painful and touching impossibility of it all might suddenly occur to the world and the world might be forced to take the moment back, to correct this moment with a sudden heaving and erasure: No, I'm sorry, but you were meant to be alone.

She was still there when he returned. She had barely moved. They said nothing as he held a match over the gas and it sprung into blue hissing flame. He boiled water. He put the soup on the flame in a blackened pot. All in silence. At last she spoke, in a quiet and sickly voice: "I thought you weren't going to come back."

When the soup was moving in its pot and giving off a cloud of fragrant steam, he lifted it from the stove and poured some into a large coffee mug, which he carried to the bed. She sat up against the wall and went pale with the effort, then took the cup from his hands. With the first sip, she retched, and let the soup fall and splash against the mattress, burning Cosimo's leg, and she curled into a ball away from him, ashamed, and began to cry.

"I'm sorry, I'm so sorry."

Cosimo said nothing, but picked up the cup, wiping it carefully. He filled it again at the stove and carried it back to the bed. She held onto it, staring at him as if he were a miracle and as she put the cup to her lips, he ran a finger through her hair, then pulled it back, going red. She swallowed a small amount of soup this time, with difficulty, then put the cup aside. She took Cosimo's hand and put it to the side of her head, which was wet with sickness. Cosimo leaned forward to kiss her on the forehead, and he could smell the fever in her hair.

She closed her eyes, to prevent revulsion, and kissed the gnarled lip. She laid her head against his neck and cried. Then she kissed him again and again with the will to drive the loathing out of him, and her, not simply to heal him but so that she would be with some-body good, who knew that he was good; this was the most important thing. And Cosimo, despite himself, began to cry as well.

They sat for a long time on that mattress, confining themselves to the soft rectangular space and filling it with their conversation, haunting it, making it different with knowledge. And as the space changed around them, the sun charted its way through the last angles of falling toward the geometrical expression of disappear-ance. Darkness. Their skin took on the faint, almost subliminal, glow that white limbs evince as the eyes begin to find them in gloom; Cosimo and Evelyn emerged slowly; they found each other.

And, as the sun examined the impossible myriad of lives teeming in dwellings and fields and roads on the other side of the blue planet, they stripped the clothing from each other as if it were bandages, carefully and with great concern, and soon their bodies were wet with the tears that the skin sheds when the eyes are closed and the anguish is indistinguishable from ecstasy.

The body examines in love every age of man and should the reader choose to look hard on the lovers, he will see, briefly, the entire cycle of transformation in the bodies themselves: the movement from the womb into the sun and strength and the terrible decay that brings flies from the air and curls flesh blackly from the bones and leaves everything glittering white in the road. And then it is over.

Cosimo and Evelyn stare at each other, breathing lightly. She takes a wet arm, tries vainly to wipe the wet salt from his forehead, and laughs.

"One day," Evelyn tells Cosimo, "one day Mary Mary is sitting in her window, and she's just . . . well, done stuff with this Roman soldier. She's putting on makeup and staring into the mirror. And right there in the mirror, she sees a little piece of the window and in that window a face.

"It's the face of this man who's riding by. He's on a donkey. It's one of those times when you see something and it just changes everything. Imagine you're just leading your ordinary life, and you see something that makes you, I don't know, want some whole new thing. Some whole new way of living, so that you can never go back to what you used to do.

"This man is not beautiful, really. But what he is is so completely at peace, and yet sad, that you want to know what it is that he's thinking: so badly that you're willing to follow him, just drop your life and follow him, until you figure out the mystery of being sad and peaceful at the same time.

"So Mary Mary sees this man and the first thing she feels is totally ashamed. Of everything she's become, of everything she is. She just wants to take every piece of herself and throw it away. So she runs out onto the street and throws herself in the path of the man with the donkey. 'Ride over me,' she says. 'I just want you to ride right over me, like I was the road. I hate myself.'

"But the man on the donkey just sits there and smiles at the woman in the road in front of him, and then he leans forward and puts out his hand. Mary Mary doesn't know what to do. She hates herself so much that she can't even begin to imagine touching this hand which is like two things: it's a human hand, attached to a man on a donkey, but it's also like an opening into another world and a tall piece of light.... She knows that if she touches that hand, she's either going to change into something beautiful or die."

•

A riel had the dream again. Two buildings, bracketing existence: one on either side, a lover on each arm. He had made the city tall, and was prepared to walk away. Wearing a long coat, with the collar turned up, Ariel took one last look at the high and lonely window, his window, and turned from his dark creation to stride down the wide road that led away from his city.

The dream would end, often, with this: Ariel striding, the cloth whirling about his legs as he moved through the night, the city that he had made diminishing behind him, finished. But, on this rather different night, during which his crippled assistant was, even then, violating the flesh of the young woman Ariel had chosen to honor with his lust, the dream found a new and disturbing conclusion.

As Ariel strode through the darkness, he heard the sound of steel against pavement: the scraping that makes sparks in the night. A whore stepped out of the shadow of a dumpster and blocked his path. She was crawling with insects and her light garment was smeared with road filth. Ariel raised a fist, but she simply stood, at her full height, and allowed the hood to fall from her tall head, revealing her face. It was the face of a Heavenly Messenger.

"I am Mary," said the angel. "I shall keep you safe in your travels, for you have built a most auspicious and extreme city. I am your angel, Ariel Price. I am for you. But..."

Yes? thought Ariel. But what? Ought there to be restrictions upon his angelic companionship? His city was very good.

"But I must insist that you go, now, along this way, and do not turn back. Do not once turn to look at the city that you have made, for it is finished."

Ariel's lip curled in disdain. He was not accustomed to restrictions. "Thank you," he said curtly. "I shall consider your advice."

"I am not advising you. I am insisting. Go now."

Ariel stared coldly at the angel and turned with deliberate inso-lence to stare fully upon the city that he had made. The angel cried once, with great anguish, and the foul rags fell from her, revealing her in naked glory so bright that Ariel would have been ashamed to look upon her. But he did not look upon her—he was gazing at his city. The angel rose on a warm current of air and floated off into the night like a lost balloon.

Ariel saw nothing of this. He was sick with watching something else: the two tallest towers, his pride and accomplishment, had, at the moment of his turning, changed to pillars of white crystal. And then, as he briefly admired the effect that these glittering pillars created against the night sky, a torrent of rain swept through the firmament, drenching the architect and his new city, and the white towers began to lose their form. The edges went soft, and then the tops washed away, and then the towers in their entirety drained, slowly but inexorably, to the gutter, reduced to watery salt.

MARGARET MORTON

Fragile Dwelling

Angelo Aldi, Pier 84, New York
Angelo Aldi built a house on Pier 84 after he could no longer afford his room in Coney Island. He identified his door with a hand-painted sign that read "Aldi," decorated the structure's exterior with stuffed animals, and created two gardens with toys and plastic plants.

The Chinese Man's Roof, Chinatown, New York
Sam Wong dug his home out of the back slope of a hill alongside the Manhattan Bridge and created a private back entrance leading to his hut. This photograph shows only the roof, which was held down with rocks.

Mr. Lee's House, Chinatown, New York
Yi Poi Lee walked the streets of Chinatown each morning, collecting the colored ropes and strings that held his house together. In May 1992, an arsonist torched the home and Lee died in the fire.

Bo's House, East River, New York
Bo built a plastic-covered home in the shadow of an elevated highway near the Manhattan Bridge. He lived there with his dog, Boy, and used shopping carts to gather building materials and to transport the cans he redeemed for a living.

Jimmy at Fish Pond, Lower East Side, New York

A Southerner, Jimmy Spence created a private oasis in an empty lot, a pond lined with plastic garbage bags and stocked with goldfish. He constructed a tent and a vegetable garden behind the pond, where he grew corn and tomatoes.

Pepe with Bible, Lower East Side, New York
Over a period of three years, Pepe Otero transformed his one-room shack in a shantytown known as Bushville into a five-room home. A former bookbinder, Pepe poses with a Bible he has bound. *I'm no architect. God is the architect, he is the best architect in town.*

Mario in Doorway, Lower East Side, New York
Mario Gomez lived in three different dwellings in Bushville. He poses here in a three-piece suit given to him by a friend in a dwelling he constructed.

The Destruction of Bushville, Lower East Side, New York
On December 15, 1993, in the early morning hours, Pepe Otero's home was razed when the community was demolished by Sanitation Department bulldozers.

Fragile Dwelling

The homeless individuals of New York City chronicled in these photographs have constructed dwellings that provide far more than mere shelter. These improvised habitats are as diverse as the people who build them and they bear witness to the profound human need to create a sense of place, no matter how extreme one's circumstances. The clusters of makeshift houses, scattered across vacant lots, public parks, along rivers, and under bridges and highway exit ramps, are constructed primarily from consumer detritus, scavenged from the streets and reconstituted as building material. They are decorated with signs, roof ornaments, porches, and gardens, and their interiors are enriched with collections of objects found on the street.

Periodically these communities are demolished by Sanitation Department bulldozers. In some cases the residents are warned in advance of the impending destruction. Few heed the warnings, however, since they have been offered no viable alternatives. When the bulldozers arrive, residents are left with only a few moments to salvage their belongings before their fragile illusions of home are turned, once again, into piles of refuse.

—Margaret Morton

Torches Mauve

(Franz Kline)

Outer space
the part of a line
that night is
how direction shifts
how up becomes
across, the dark is
light
dissolving; it fades,
recedes until darks
become colors, or
parts of colors,
nowhere else
to look, no sense
of any other no
nowhere beyond.

Blueberry Eyes

(Franz Kline)

Let's fight to hold
the darkness off

somewhere, the other
side of, the river

the shadow of a
bridge, let's let

the night begin
to echo & watch

as flashes of light
bounce off the flow

of water below.
On board a train

New York is
wilderness

bridges connect
deserted islands

remain as sun dis-
appears behind the

Palisades, greens
turn to yellow

red & swirls to
stop at Spuyten Duyvil

& in that instant
train & landscape

intersect &
sunlight dies.

His Wedding

Either my lover has done something he didn't want to do or I don't know him. Our eyes meet, but at this moment he is really just the bridegroom of a young Turkish woman; she is sitting at his side. He looks at me the way he looks at the other two hundred people—for barely a second. Two criminals in the dock: that's how he and his bride seem at their small table. All the guests in the room are looking at the couple, and the couple is looking at the floor. It wouldn't have taken much for me to be next to him, in a white gown; I'm not sure whether his bride knows this. For a year I turned down each of his proposals. I didn't let him bury me in a foreign family.

This is the last time that his family will offer me a place at their table. I sit at the border between close and distant relatives. Here two tables come together. A crack appears where the rounded edges meet. All the tables are covered with paper. Gradually I give up hope of seeing my lover in private. I draw on the smooth surface. I draw quickly without putting down the pencil, as is my habit when I'm agitated. The couple, the couple, the couple. No one catches on to the drawing. For me every stroke is evocation:

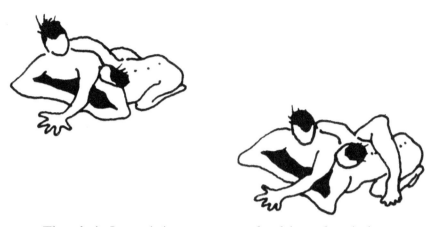

The chair I am sitting on was wedged into the circle as an afterthought. I have to make up my mind on which side of the table legs I should place my feet: to the right, toward the sisters, who are squeezed together as it is; or to the left, toward the uncle, who's flown in from Adana. He doesn't know a word of German. Naturally I opt for the sisters.

I've spent the entire day with them. They've taken care of me and spoken to me as if I were their girlfriend. In the morning, shortly after my arrival, we compared our evening gowns, and they showed me their jewelry. They felt very sorry for me because I had none, and they lent me a necklace. There was so much to talk about. Whenever my lover's name came up, the sisters held their tongues or steered the conversation toward a different subject. They seemed to fear unexpected questions. My lover's parents had never spoken to me much. They had never asked about my family or about my work. They had always said hello and goodbye to me, and in between they had spoken their own language. It was they who engineered this wedding.

The father sits at the head of the table. He sends me a glass of whisky. It's full to the brim. The father raises his arm and toasts me without looking at me. I have no choice. The father's wife, my lover's mother (who brought me the whisky), whispers with the sisters; she urges me to drink. Then she mentions that the couple's bed has not been delivered in time, and again I think about the coming night. Next to the mother stands, elegantly dressed, the silent aunt. That's what everybody calls her because she never speaks. My lover claims he has heard her speak only three times in his life. The last time, she asked him to get engaged.

In November, my lover told me he was getting married but we were not yet defeated by time. And the bride's time had not yet begun.

This morning my lover sent me to the hairdresser with his sisters. We were supposed to look alike for the coming celebration. The bride sat in front of a round mirror. She contemplated herself as if she were alone in the world. She was pale, and her face showed only that she wanted to do a good job of it. She endured the occasion as she would have any other. A hairdresser was curling waves into her girlish hair. It was the most modern salon in town. Another bride was waiting by the cash register. She sat erect, her eyes glued to the salon's proprietor, who was doing one sister's hair. The waiting bride held her veil and wreath ready in her lap. The proprietor tried to calm her with small gestures. But every bride is short of time. While the hairdresser was constructing my coiffure, my lover came through the door. He looked at his bride—a look I had thought only I could inspire. The bride stood up, and my lover disappeared with her, arm in arm. No sooner did they arrive somewhere than a new commitment tore them away again. The image of the fleeing couple haunted the day until evening. It gave the out-of-town guests the feeling that they could never see enough of this couple: it made them look forward to the celebration even more eagerly.

My hair curves over my forehead. It feels like a doll's hair. Distant relatives stop and praise my hairdo instead of praising me. Probably nobody knows why I'm here. I know why. I figured that by watching the couple I would understand where the three of us stood with one another. I'm still afraid of public displays of affection between them; but so far there have been none. I did not attend the ceremony. The imam came into the house while I was adorning myself with the sisters. An ordinary meeting room, somewhere in the countryside. Everything is forbidden in that room. The windows must not be opened, the lights not dimmed, the radiators not turned on. It is an icy day near Christmas. We had to put up garlands and balloons with tape—no nails must be hammered into the walls. I taped a big paper heart to the couple's table.

Next the sisters showed me the bridegroom's new apartment. My lover's family seems to have only one piece of kitchen furniture: the corner bench; and only one piece of furniture fits inside the living room, behind the couch: the armoire; in the bedroom where the only furnishing is the marriage bed, there is an extra-wide mattress. In all the rooms, carpets on white tiled floors. The windows of the neighboring house shimmered through the curtains. It was as if every wall in the apartment bore a word that everyone knew but no one uttered: blood. She would bleed here. And suddenly I wanted to go to him.

The sisters wouldn't leave my side. We changed clothes. The celebration began. The newlyweds came into the room past a guard of honor made up of couples.

The children are already scurrying amid gaudy shreds of paper. More and more decorations are falling from the ceiling and floating down to the guests. The children gather the shreds and fight over them. Their parents form a long line in front of the married couple and hand over the gifts. My lover's brother thanks people through a microphone. He names the source and the contents of each package. *Cay servisi*—tea service—seems to be the most frequent phrase. His voice sounds like that of a local politician on the campaign trail. I remain alone at the family table. My lover is so close to me that it never occurred to me to get him a present. I could have given him a drawing. But the sketch I tear out of the paper tablecloth looks wretched. And my lover values things that look like something: watches, attaché cases.

Soon long rows of pinned banknotes dangle over the chests of the bride and the groom, as if they had sold themselves to the rest of the company. I should have warned him. My lover probably didn't know how dangerous rituals can be. One ritual is followed by another, and in the end you are buried.

How earnest, by contrast, was the movement with which he shoved his cock between my lips.

The wall of presents grows higher and higher behind the couple. I leave the room. What comes next is cake, music, and belly-dancing by the guests—I see my lover's hips from a distance. (I've never figured out where that movement actually begins: his hips look as if they were floating away. I've watched him, I've filmed him, I've put my hands on his belly, but I've never understood the source of the movement.) One of the sisters beckons me into the kitchen. One hundred and sixty fruit cakes, cheese cakes, and cream cakes have to be cut. The knives are dull, bits of cake stick to them and can be wiped off only with fingers. Though I keep licking my fingers, they remain sticky. Every square inch of my skin, my clothes—everything is sticky and cold. I turn and see my lover vanishing inside the cold storage room for drinks. When I open the door, he has his back to me. Don't catch cold, he says. I enter. It won't take long. Without lifting my arms, I put them around his belly. He's expecting me. I hold his tip between my two fingers—a dark berry that I squeeze. That's enough. When I leave, my hand is a fist. No one in the kitchen notices. Everyone's hand is dripping with something.

An hour later, my lover's brother drives me to the hotel where my lover has paid for the room. Although I've shaken countless hands, my fingers are still sticky. The bridal couple drives ahead of us. Christmas stars hang over the streets like a last-ditch effort to postpone the end of the holiday; all I can see is her veil, which fills the entire rear window. Have I taken something from her? Now the car beeps—hands wave, two faces in the rear window—I've already turned into a side street.

I'm tired and sad. The bride won't replace me. I'll often be able to put my arms around my lover. He wouldn't even ward me off today. What bothers me is the loss of his family. Never again will I sit in their midst, respected yet left alone. My hotel room is spacious. All the objects are the same color. I switch the light off immediately. I lie in bed and feel restless. No one, other than my parents, has the right to think about me for the next few days.

Translated from the German by Joachim Neugroschel

Works on Paper

Nothing at All Richard Dadd, 1992.
Graphite on paper, 41 $\frac{1}{4}$ x 27 $\frac{1}{2}$ in.
p. 73

Untitled, 1992.
Graphite on paper, 41 $\frac{1}{8}$ x 27 $\frac{3}{8}$ in.
p. 74

Untitled, 1992.
Eight-color lithograph, 38 $\frac{3}{4}$ x 31 $\frac{1}{8}$ in.
p. 75

Untitled, 1992.
Etching, 43 $\frac{1}{2}$ x 52 $\frac{9}{16}$ in.
p. 76

Untitled, 1993.
Watercolor on paper, 40 $\frac{7}{8}$ x 27 $\frac{5}{8}$ in.
p. 77

Untitled, 1993–1994.
Pastel, charcoal, pencil on paper, 27 $\frac{5}{8}$ x 49 $\frac{3}{4}$ in.
pp. 78-79

Untitled, 1994.
Lithograph, 36 $\frac{1}{4}$ x 30 $\frac{1}{2}$ in.
p. 80

74

Coastline

how we can be made out of stone
or resemble an ancient coastline. . . .
in the blink of the brightness,
look at the land around us, how the sky
gets to us, height and distance—
there's so much to be desired,
it's like drowning:
the regret of drowning
is the loss
of a narrow escape,
as men can do,
lying out in the sun
when they've been drinking
and the light on the current
is a line between us and the unreachable:
when we sleep on the beach,
we do so out of faith
in our dreams we believe
in the chance to escape
to be pushed off into
nothing like a bird, a flying fish
gulping, an undertow around
each ankle, an angel,
a welder on a bridge
we float under
waving.

Mals Mots: Aphorisms— Sweet and Sour—By an Anti-Hero Architect

Valid Rantings

Double curse in this day: an architect whose work is mannerist and well-mannered.

I am an exhibitionist: I go around exposing my doubts.

What a shame to justify rather than design.

When we were young we had to suffer upright, uptight, sanctimonious, and pious-reformist-progressive Modernists in architecture—now we are old we have to suffer regressive, perfectionist-historicist-preservationists, purist urbanists, or expressionistic egoists in architecture.

The unforgiving medium: you can't modify or edit the work once it's up.

Hype Critics: Journalism

Journalists like spectacular architecture: it makes their job easier.

You're never sure you're good unless you're ignored or controversial.

No good art can be universally liked in its time: the problem is to make it so the right people hate it.

What's retardataire to an avant-garde critic is often avant-garde.

Purposeful misunderstanding can be a technique of criticism.

There is little understanding of architecture these days—the art of it, the sweat, the subtlety.

Hype Theories: Avant-Garde

What's with this artistic originality stuff that the Modernists derived from the Romantic movement—when the history of architecture is dominated by: sublime English Gothic derived from the French, sublime English Renaissance derived from the Italians, sublime Renaissance architecture derived from ancient Rome, sublime ancient Roman architecture derived from Greece; why can't our architecture derive and represent all kinds of things for our complex and contradictory age of multiversalism?

If you're really avant-garde you don't know it.

Good art involves fractions of inches as well as ideas.

I'll take the vulgar over the pretentious any day.

No God in the details today—only ideology in the concepts.

Ideology is the last refuge of scoundrels.

The trouble used to be architects read only one book—now they read too many books (or pretend to).

Peter Eisenman says he gets his best ideas in the shower but I think he gets them from books he hasn't read.

Let us remember our American genius for plain speech and pragmatic content—not pretentious, not heroic, not esoteric—that of Emerson, Thoreau, Lincoln, Hemingway—which must not be substituted by perfumed shit.

Hype Buildings: Decon-ism

Admitted pastiche is better than disguised pastiche.

It can be said the Neo-Modern vocabulary of today or that of Deconstructionism represents a revival—indeed, a revival of a revival, that of the International Style, itself derived from an early-twentieth-century industrial vernacular, and it sits rather at home as a style among styles within the reviled context of postmodernism—and it accommodates at the same time to the hype sensibility of today as it promotes punk and blue trusses as appliqué and floors and walls as ramps: it engages the vulgarity of Las Vegas in terms of hype-forms but not commercial symbols—it represents the easy-heroic stance of today—like a Poussin landscape with plastic gods in an Arcadian Disneyland.

Try to be constructive—do not try to be destructive—or else you will risk being more adolescent than significant.

Exception as a motif should be an oxymoron.

All bravado is no bravado.

Consistent inconsistency and flamboyant inconsistency are both a bore.

Architecture is not an aria all the time playing.

Naughty boys are cute as they get attention—up to a point—in life as in architecture.

The safety, the prestige, the journalistic appeal of the extremist position.

If you are not turned on by the idea of shelter probably you should not be an architect but a sculptor; if not turned on by architecture but by theory you should probably be a philosopher.

I Love Mannerism

Viva a fragment that implies a whole.

Richness and ambiguity over simplicity and clarity: down with Minimalism that your work brags of.

On being a mannerist architect: you are either vilified or ignored.

Beautiful lessons via Beethoven via Toscanini: non-ending themes as fragments within the movement as a whole; lyrical and dissonant juxtapositions to promote supreme tension/sublime affirmation.

It's as important to make a plan as it is not to follow it.

Urbanism: Design and Bureaucracy

Making history is as important as preserving history.

Awkwardness is part of growth and growth is part of vitality.

Beware of urban do-gooders.

The only thing worse than a corrupt bureaucracy is a zealous bureaucracy.

Today architects frequently submit to taste qualification committees set up by architects who haven't made it representing community groups who don't get it.

In the old days when experts rather than consensus held sway you got a lot of shit, but the system did not preclude some good coming out of it.

Generally the people who are most critical of Disney have bad taste.

Pseudo-urbanity—closing off streets and littering them with *objets*.

Originators and Followers

The only thing worse than being ignored is being imitated—although your followers, as part of their perversity, disguise their source.

If you're lucky you live long enough to see the bad results of your good ideas.

Your followers sometimes do it before you.

If you're good you're misinterpreted.

Your followers say you didn't go far enough with the original idea.

The fate of someone who has been influential: your original contribution has been forgotten because your idea has become pervasive— or you're blamed for the misinterpretations of it that have become perverse.

An original artist is not necessarily a good artist; a good artist is not necessarily an original artist.

I've been wrong a lot and now my wrongs are clichés.

Anti-Heroism and the Sublime Ordinary

Pay homage to the nerd in life and art.

The universal ideal as it emerged in architecture is more vividly observed in the fast food realm of McDonald's and Pizza Huts all over the world than in the realm of heroic architecture.

Mass culture is as relevant as high culture.

Work to be of your time and then you will be ahead of your time.

I love the Swiss chalet, the generic house and barn, that exemplifies architecture as shelter at an almost Japanese extreme—and whose lyrical eaves protect people, animals, structure, and ornament below.

Look at artists' lofts or Edison's labs—as well as the Italian palace and Nassau Hall—and you see the significance of generic place for functional activity and evolution.

Iconography

Viva iconography and scenography in Las Vegas now—and soon all over.

Houston: a beautiful American city—except the billboards aren't big enough; how sad that legislation is at work to diminish the poignant, colorful, and scale-ful juxtapositions of billboards and bungalows beyond the highways.

Since the late Middle Ages no vocabulary or style of architecture has been totally original or not somehow based on a style of the past— Renaissance, Baroque, Neo-Classicism, Eclecticism, Modernism—the latter based on American industrial vernacular architecture or industrial engineering forms—except for Rococo, Art Nouveau, and some Frank Lloyd Wright: let us now abandon our hopeless search for new forms and define the artful dimension of architecture as iconographic.

Learning From Now

Learning from everything.

Flights of fancy start from the elemental fundamental.

The assurance of the naive surrounds us.

The Box

There are forces in the outside world, and here within our borders," said the Prime Minister, fixing Quentin with an accusing stare, "who seek to overthrow my government by violent means. They wish to create the impression that we are weak, that we will capitulate. They even go so far as to suggest that the country is in a state of civil war. I say to these cowards—for that is what they are—that they will have to face up to reality. And the reality is that every act of cowardly violence will harden our resolve. The reality is that my government is committed to the maintenance of law and order."

Quentin put down the bottle of Southern Comfort and went to stand in front of the television set. "He's out of his mind," he said sadly. "That is the horrible truth. He's mad as a hatter."

The Prime Minister's face filled the screen. It looked as soft and pliable as a lump of clay.

"Do you mind not standing in front of the screen," Mary said.

Quentin ignored her, and she moved to the other end of the sofa.

"Who seek to sow the seeds of discord and reap a harvest of bloody revolution," the Prime Minister said.

The camera began to zoom out and the Prime Minister grew smaller and smaller, until he was just six inches tall. He was seated behind a desk in an office filled with leather-bound books. He rose and came slowly round to the front of the desk.

"To those who approach us as equals in the community of nations, we extend the hand of friendship."

A chubby hand reached out to Quentin. He put out his own hand and it tingled as it approached the screen and then slipped through into warm custard. The screen went blank and Quentin groped, closed his fingers around the Prime Minister, and jerked him out of the box.

In Quentin's fist, the Prime Minister looked even tinier than he had on the screen. He flashed and flickered, filling the space around him with a dirty cloud of electrons. "Put me back! Put me back this instant!" he shouted, beating his tiny fists on Quentin's knuckles.

Quentin turned to Mary, who was getting shakily to her feet, and said, "Look what I just did."

"You can't do this!" the Prime Minister yelled. "By the powers vested in me I command you to put me back where you found me."

The voice was so full of authority and indignation that Quentin almost obeyed.

He took one step toward the television set. But then the Prime Minister sank his teeth into Quentin's forefinger, and Quentin gasped and dropped him. He careened off Quentin's knee, arms and legs flailing, and fell with a soft thud on a beanbag. He jumped to his feet immediately, looked challengingly around him, and began to scramble down to the carpet.

"Get something to catch him in," Quentin said.

Mary ran to the kitchen. When she came back into the lounge with a salad bowl, the Prime Minister was wobbling toward the television set. Quentin headed him off with a rolled-up newspaper and she dropped the bowl over him. There was a scratching sound against the inside of the bowl, and it inched forward. Then silence. Mary sat down on the arm of the sofa and looked at the message on the screen. We apologize for the short delay, it said, our technicians are working on the problem.

"I hope we didn't hurt him," Mary said.

"Of course not," Quentin replied, nudging the bowl with his toe, "the little bastard's as hard as nails."

Then he sat down heavily on the sofa and looked at his hand.

They sat in silence, Mary chewing her fingernails and Quentin drinking from the bottle, until the Prime Minister's office reappeared on the screen. A reporter was standing to attention in front of the desk. "Sorry about the break in transmission," he said. "We're sad to announce that the Prime Minister has suddenly taken ill and his address to the nation is therefore necessarily postponed. His doctor assures us that his condition is not serious. We will be issuing a full statement later this evening."

"Do you think he's all right?" Mary said. "He's very quiet in there."

When Quentin didn't answer she went to the bowl, lifted it cautiously, and peeped under it. "He's not moving," she said over her shoulder. Quentin studied the level of the liquor in the bottle.

Mary prodded the inert form with her finger. "Oh God," she said, "I think he's dead."

Quentin sighed and squatted down beside her. "Just answer me one simple question. Do we like him?"

"That doesn't matter," she replied. "He's human, isn't he?"

"Have we ever liked him?" he insisted.

"No," she was forced to admit.

"Then why the hell should we start liking him now?"

The Prime Minister groaned and sat up, rubbing his head.

"He's not even dead," Quentin said. He picked the Prime Minister up by the scruff of his neck and shook him. Then he held him up to his face and said, "Now what should we do with you?"

The Prime Minister began to struggle, kicking and punching at the air. Quentin smiled and rocked him back and forth.

"Please, Quentin," Mary said, tugging at his sleeve.

"All right then. What do you think we should do with him?"

"We could keep him. . . ."

"Keep him!"

"My mother has a printer's tray full of little things that would be perfect for him: beer mugs, teacups—"

"Who's going to feed him?" Quentin demanded.

"We could take turns."

"Out of the question. Here, hold him while I have a piss."

When he returned, Mary was sitting on the sofa with the Prime Minister cradled in her palm, his arms folded and his chin on his chest. Quentin sat down next to Mary and put his arm around her shoulders. He examined the bald patch on the back of the Prime Minister's head. Then he kissed Mary's ear and whispered, "You're right. It could be a lot of fun to keep him—for a while, at least."

Mary crept down the passage, avoiding the floorboards she knew would creak, and peered into the kitchen. She could see the cage on the counter of the breakfast nook, bathed in cold moonlight from the window. She went closer slowly. The Prime Minister had his back to her. He was slumped—disconsolately, she thought—on a pile of sunflower seeds, with his head resting against the bars. He had taken off his jacket and folded it into a pillow, and that was under his neck; he had loosened his tie and slipped his braces off his shoulders. His feet were propped up on a corner of the water bowl. As she watched, one hand moved up to his face and a pinprick of coal glowed briefly. There was a pause, and then a small cloud of baby-blue smoke drifted up. Mary pulled up a stool and rested her elbows on the counter so that her face was just inches from the bars.

The Prime Minister's eyes were closed. He could have been asleep, except that his hand rose and fell, and his face brightened and faded in the glow from his cigarette.

Mary tapped a fingernail on one of the bars. The Prime Minister's lip curled and then his eyes opened slowly and looked into hers.

"Hello," she said, smiling.

He stared at her.

She reached a finger in through the bars and scratched the side of his head. He jerked his head away, strode angrily to the other side of the cage and sat down with his back to her.

Mary turned the cage around so that she could see his face. "You're incredibly cute," she said.

The Prime Minister ground his cigarette out, lay down on his side, and pulled the collar of his shirt up over his ears.

After a while Quentin called from the bedroom and Mary went back to bed.

The first meal Mary gave the Prime Minister consisted of a morsel of mashed potato, a sliver of steak, and a pea, all carefully laid out in the lid of a milk bottle. The Prime Minister took one look at it and threw it in a corner. The whole of the next day he refused to eat. On the following morning he ate some oats and a raisin, and banged his plate against the bars for more.

That night Mary got up for some water and heard a strange squeaking sound coming from the kitchen. Going quietly nearer she saw the Prime Minister, stripped to his underpants, with his tie knotted around his head, jogging in the treadmill.

And in this haphazard fashion things settled into a routine.

Mary fed the Prime Minister and saw to it that his cage was kept clean. She provided him with little things from toy shops, most of which he threw out of the cage when her back was turned. The one object he seemed pleased with was a recliner, complete with a miniature antimacassar and lace-edged scatter cushions. One morning Mary found the Prime Minister's clothes in a pile next to his breakfast dishes, so she washed them for him. She also gave him a bowl of water and retired discreetly to another room. Though she heard him singing as he splashed around in the bath, he still refused to speak to her.

Mary found the Prime Minister fascinating. She spent hours each day watching him as he paced around with his hands clasped behind his back, or sat daydreaming in his chair, or did his exercises. In the evenings, after Quentin came in from work, Mary had to watch over the Prime Minister to protect him.

Quentin's hatred for the Prime Minister did not diminish with time. He seized every opportunity to torment him. He poured water over him, he threatened him with cigarette lighters, he banged things down on the counter next to the cage when he was napping. Every evening over supper, while the Prime Minister ate his miniature version of the meal with his back purposefully turned, Quentin would read out the latest official news.

"This morning the Prime Minister was discharged from hospital. His doctor is still refusing to comment on the precise nature of the illness that struck him down mysteriously last Saturday. However, he described his condition as satisfactory. After his discharge, the Prime Minister retired to his country residence to recuperate."

The Prime Minister would carry on chewing as if he hadn't heard.

Only once did Mary feel the desire to hurt him, and this was in an attempt to provoke him out of his stubborn silence. She was washing the dishes one morning, chatting away to him about her childhood, her parents, her sister who had emigrated, and looked up to see that he wasn't listening at all. He was lying on his back examining the mechanism of the treadmill. She grabbed an old newspaper off the vegetable rack and was about to bang on the cage with it, but her eye caught the headline and instead she tore off the front page and stuffed it in through the bars. She smiled as the Prime Minister wrestled with it and then, when he had succeeded in spreading it out, paced out its meaning with his hands behind his back and a tear on his cheek. The page showed a photograph of the Prime Minister's wife, smiling bravely into the camera, and below that a report to the effect that the Prime Minister was still not well enough to speak to reporters. There was also an editorial which speculated that the Prime Minister's political career was over, and listed the five people most likely to succeed him. When he wrung his hands over that, Mary started to laugh. The Prime Minister flew into a rage, overturning his chair and kicking sawdust through the bars.

After this incident Mary felt terrible. She apologized at length, assuring him that she wasn't really at all like Quentin, but the Prime Minister maintained a wounded silence.

One evening the three of them were watching television. At Mary's insistence the Prime Minister's cage had been placed on a kitchen stool quite close to the set. Although she had motivated the concession to Quentin on humanitarian grounds, her main concern was to keep a protective eye on the Prime Minister.

During the commercial break before the late news, the Prime Minister heaved himself out of his chair and went to urinate in the cup Mary had provided for that purpose in a corner of his cage.

Quentin suddenly burst out: "That's it! I can't take it any more!" He grabbed the cage and stormed through to the kitchen.

"Please, Quentin," Mary pleaded, running after him.

Quentin put the plug in the sink and turned on the water. "I won't tolerate his presence in this house another minute!" he shouted. "What the hell are we going to do with him? We can't just keep him until he dies. He could live for another thirty years." He turned off the tap and reached into the cage. The Prime Minister clung tenaciously to the bars, but one firm tug was enough to pull him loose. Mary flung herself on Quentin but he shoved her away and plunged the Prime Minister under the water.

A stream of bubbles boiled to the surface.

"He's talking underwater," Mary said in a small voice.

Quentin pulled the Prime Minister out of the water and threw him down on the counter. "This is fucking impossible!" he shouted, and went back to the lounge to watch the news.

Mary put her finger on the Prime Minister's damp belly and pressed. Water spilled from the slack lips, and then his chest shuddered and began to rise and fall. She lifted him gently, laid him out on a dishcloth, and blew in his face. After a while he stirred and sat up, choking. He was trying to say something. Mary patted him on his back.

"He's crazy," the Prime Minister finally said in a gush of water.

"There, there," Mary said, pushing him down onto his back, "you must rest. You've been through a horrible experience."

The Prime Minister lay quietly for several minutes while Mary stroked his forehead. Then he pushed himself tiredly into a sitting position. "Under the circumstances," he said, choking back a sob, "I'm ready to talk."

I t was a formal meeting, with Mary in the chair. Quentin sat on a stool at one end of the breakfast-nook counter, the Prime Minister sat in his recliner at the other. The cage had been put away where he couldn't see it. Once he was out of the cage the Prime Minister seemed to grow in stature. He sat with an air of dignified despair, appropriate to an honorable surrender, his fingers meshed together in his lap, his legs crossed, one shiny black shoe swinging.

"I declare this meeting open," Mary said.

The Prime Minister rose, looked around the room as if acknowledging a silent audience, then cleared his throat and began: "Ladies and gentlemen. You see before you a man who was once the proud leader—"

"You're not half the man you used to be," Quentin put in.

The Prime Minister looked gravely at the toe of his shoe, then began again. "Ladies and gentlemen. My friend's manner may be insulting, but there is a measure of truth in his words. I stand before you alone, humiliated—"

"Belittled," Quentin said.

The Prime Minister stamped his foot. He addressed himself to the chair. "In the name of decency, will you stop this man from interrupting me."

"Please, Quentin," Mary said, "let him have his say."

"He's not in parliament now," Quentin said.

"My boy . . . ," the Prime Minister said.

"Ha!" Quentin shouted, banging his fist on the counter so hard that the Prime Minister lost his footing and fell on his hands and knees. Quentin burst out laughing. The Prime Minister picked himself up, dusted the knees of his suit, and sat down in his recliner. He crossed his legs deliberately and said, "I demand an apology for this childish behavior." Mary looked at Quentin.

"You're not serious," he said.

He saw that she was.

There was a silence during which Quentin tapped his cigarette on the edge of the ashtray and the Prime Minister rubbed his knees.

At last Quentin said, "I'm sorry."

"Apology accepted," the Prime Minister said.

"Let's begin again then," Mary said. "Quentin, please control your temper. Mr. Prime Minister—proceed, and please make it brief."

"Ladies and gentlemen. Forgive me if I do not rise. Through no fault of my own, my knees hurt. Let me come straight to the point. What we have here is a classic case of interdependence. I need you, for practical reasons: food, water, a roof over my head. Incidentally, the question of living quarters is one I'd like to come back to later on. As I was saying, I need you. You also need me. The reasons you need me are rather different. I amuse you. I keep you company. Don't think I haven't noticed the dearth of human fellowship around here. But perhaps I could come back to that as well later on."

The meeting lasted four hours. Quentin smoked fifteen cigarettes. The Prime Minister, who was dying for a cigarette himself, bit his nails and jogged his foot. He wrung his hands. He limped around on the counter waving his fist and wagging his finger. Quentin spat at him and bombed him with peanuts. Eventually the Prime Minister, in a frenzy of frustration at his inability to overturn the ashtray, scooped up handfuls of ash and rubbed them into his face.

At last the meeting was over. The minutes, as Mary set them down, recorded that:

1) Quentin would attempt to secure the Prime Minister's wife without using unnecessary force or causing her unnecessary anguish.

2) The Prime Minister's living quarters would be improved.

3) Quentin would refrain from taunting the Prime Minister without due cause.

4) The Prime Minister, in turn, would do his best not to antagonize Quentin by refraining from, among other things, urinating in his presence or trying to escape.

After the meeting Mary installed the Prime Minister in one corner of the spare room. The Prime Minister, in his new spirit of conciliation, offered to carry the recliner through himself, but eventually gave up halfway down the passage and allowed Mary to carry him and his furniture the rest of the way.

That night the Prime Minister couldn't sleep. He roamed the expanses of the wall-to-wall carpet and charted the limits of his new homeland.

For seven full evenings they sat in front of the television set, Quentin perched on a stool within easy reach of the screen, hands tingling, the Prime Minister in his recliner on top of another stool, holding thumbs conspicuously, Mary sitting quietly on the sofa behind them.

Getting the Prime Minister had been a simple enough task; getting his wife proved to be more difficult. It required calculations of scale and definition that hadn't occurred to Quentin before. In the weeks after her husband vanished she made frequent appearances on the box (or in the box, as Quentin put it). They saw her almost every night, looking bravely into the camera and describing a relapse or a recovery. But the camera was usually focused on her face, and the opportunity for snatching her was lost. On the one occasion when she was shown in full figure, she must have been all of twelve inches tall, and Quentin, on the point of making a grab for her, saw the look of horror on the Prime Minister's face and stopped himself.

On the eighth evening the Prime Minister's wife suddenly appeared in perfect proportion. In the middle of a car chase, the screen went blank, a voice said, "We interrupt this transmission for a special news report," and there she was. She was floating in a cloud of peach chiffon and she was weeping. In the distance behind her a flag was flying at half-mast. There was one small problem: standing next to her, with one hand on her elbow and a grim expression on his face, was a man in a military uniform. He was wearing a peaked cap and there was a bright row of medals on his tunic.

"Now!" cried the Prime Minister, jumping to his feet.

"Don't," said Mary.

The Prime Minister's wife dabbed at her eyes; the Minister of Defense opened his mouth to speak. And at that moment Quentin plunged his arm in up to the elbow and scooped.

A broken flagpole, trailing gravel and sparks, a whirl of peach chiffon and a blur of khaki exploded into the room.

The Prime Minister's wife landed on a fern in one corner of the room, and that broke her fall. The Minister of Defense struck Quentin in the chest, rebounded, and, borne down by the weight of his medals, dropped headfirst toward the floor. Quentin dived from the stool and caught him just before he hit the carpet.

The Prime Minister shouted "Gys!" in a voice so loud it could have belonged to a fully grown man.

The Minister of Defense scrambled out of Quentin's grasp and ran several paces, then threw himself on the carpet, rolled over, and rose up on one knee with a revolver in his hand. He pulled the trigger and Quentin felt a sharp sting on his cheek. Quentin swatted the Minister with the back of his hand and was surprised to see him fly across the room, smash into the wall, and drop in a heap onto the carpet.

Mary turned the body over. The head was caved in like an eggshell and leaking. She began to drop large tears onto the corpse. The Prime Minister had meanwhile slid down the leg of the stool and retrieved his wife from the potted plant. The chiffon was a little bruised, but otherwise she seemed to be in good health. After a brief embrace, they went over to the body; and now the Prime Minister's wife began to wail, and her wails rose up to meet Mary's large sobs.

Quentin stormed out in pursuit of a drink.

Mary recovered the body from the rubbish bin and did her best to straighten it out. She wiped the blood off its face and pulled up the knot of its tie. She put the cap on its head and rearranged the medals. Then she fetched a spade from under the kitchen sink and buried it, with due ceremony, at the bottom of the garden.

The Prime Minister and his wife stood solemnly at the graveside. The Prime Minister made a short speech in which he praised the deceased's devotion to duty. The Prime Minister's wife sang a plaintive hymn, which almost started Mary crying again.

The following night, just before the epilogue, Quentin took the managing director of a supermarket chain. Mary gave him blankets and food and took him through to the spare room. She introduced him to the Prime Minister and his wife, and left them to make one another's acquaintance.

Quentin was lying in bed with his hands behind his head. Mary sat down on the edge of the bed next to him. "We need to talk about this thing," she said.

"I agree," Quentin said, sitting up. "It can't go on like this."

"I'm glad you also think so," she said.

"So far it's been far too random," he went on. "One here, one there. What we need's a strategy. Maybe a list." He scratched around on the bedside table for a pen and paper.

"That's not what I had in mind. I don't think you should be doing this."

"Why not?"

"Why?"

"I'm not sure yet," he said, "but I think it will become clearer as we go along. Right. Who's next?" He opened a notebook and poised a pen over the page.

"I don't want to play this game," Mary said.

"It's not a game. It's serious stuff."

"Let's forget it. I don't like you like this."

"Well, I've given you a chance," Quentin said. "If you don't want to take it, fine. Who's that woman with the face—you know, the TV personality, the one you said looked like a basset?"

The next evening Quentin took a continuity announcer whose vivacious insincerity particularly annoyed him. Mary took the hysterical woman through to the bathroom to calm her down, and while she was in there Quentin took the captain of the Northern Transvaal squash team and a country-and-western duo. When Mary came out of the spare room, having handed the continuity announcer into the capable hands of the Prime Minister's wife, she heard a tiny rendition of *Oh, Lonesome Me* coming from the lounge, and she locked herself in the bedroom and cried herself to sleep. Quentin slept on the sofa.

In the week that followed, Quentin concentrated on priests, aiming for a representative selection of denominations. The week after that, he told Mary over supper, it would be professors.

"We can't have a stupid republic developing here," he said.

Mary gave all the new people blankets and put them in the spare room. In the mornings she put in a large bowl of ProNutro; in the evenings she dished up a third plate of food and put that in the room. Every two or three days she went in with a broom and swept out the rubbish and the bodies.

The professor week didn't work out too well. After an argument with a professor of divinity, Quentin changed his mind, and started taking handfuls of spectators at sports events. "Ordinary people, that's what we need," he said to Mary, who was standing by with a picnic basket to ferry the new arrivals through.

Mary was awakened one night by a rumbling of voices. It was a small noise, far away and muted, and not altogether unpleasant. She lay listening to the sound as it rose and fell in the room next door.

"Are you awake?" Quentin said.

"Yes," she answered, turning on her side to face him.

"I've been meaning to talk to you," he said. "The spare room's starting to smell. Maybe it would be better if you cleaned it every day."

The evening after Mary left, Quentin misjudged his timing and took the torso of an opera singer. He watched the thing thumping its stumps on the carpet. Then he took a mouth out of a toothpaste ad and propped it up on a coffee table. It smiled at him. He smiled back. He speared the torso on the end of a fork and brushed it against the teeth. The lips slobbered open and the teeth began to gnash. For the hell of it, he took the leg of a statue, half a building, and a cubic meter of Indian Ocean. Then he gathered it all up and went through to the spare room.

UFOs

WHO IS INSIDE THE FLYING SAUCERS?

by Gerald Heard, August 17, 1953

The saucers are soaring again. Not that these unidentified aerial objects had ceased to scour the sky, but our attention wanes. We get tired of any mystery, even the most thrilling, if it will not give itself away. And till now the saucers have been silent. Even as they swoop across the heavens, very seldom does the faintest sound come down to us. On the few occasions that it does it is no more than the high piercing note we might expect our atmosphere would admit when slit by a flying blade.

But now we are again sitting up and taking notice of saucer reports. Why? Because many people, who have for six queer years (since, in the summer of '47, saucers first made front-page news) been critical collectors of this baffling data, have in the last few months begun to face a new question. Are the saucers so dumb as they seemed? Till now, opinion among collectors was divided, precisely as it is divided in that other thorny subject, psychical research. On the one hand were lined up the stern but open-minded critics who said, "Unidentified aerial objects exist. They are mainly disk-shaped. They dodge like snipe (or humming birds). They speed like meteors: some

Cruces, New Mexico, 3/18/1967: A New Mexico State University student took this photo of what he says is an Unidentified Flying Object while photographing land for a geology class. The object made no noise and disappeared as he looked down to change plates in the camera.

Top: Paris, 1/6/1958: The "flying saucers" apparently orbiting around the Eiffel Tower in this unretouched photograph hoax are actually reflections of lamps and their shades in the window of the Palais de Chaillot.

Inset: Wall Township, New Jersey, 3/1966: Photograph taken by a thirteen-year-old boy walking his dog. The boy turned the photograph over to the Army.

Top: Climax, Colorado, 11/16/1967: A field technician at the mountain laboratory weather station on Chalk Mountain discovered this unidentified object on his negative after he shot a roll of film in the area.

Bottom: Amarillo, Texas, undated: A farmer from Loco, Texas told a polygraph operator that this Polaroid snap shows an alien spacecraft 80 to 100 feet long.

have been timed at 18,000 m.p.h. There is also some undeniable evidence that they are radioactive or surrounded by a radioactive field. For Geiger counters double their discharge, tick twice as fast, when a disk is overhead. Beyond this we know nothing. All else is empty speculation shot through by the impudent fireworks of fraud."

So those who accept that such objects exist (and no one who has investigated the official evidence can doubt it) are bound also to sift critically and patiently any evidence for landings. Such a thing could have taken place. Then where and when and how many people saw it? As time has gone on the investigation has become more intimate, closer-up. And when we think it over, that surely is what we should expect. If the disks are from out of this world, they would be bigger fools than their design-power indicates if they thrust their attentions on us before being as sure of our intentions as long distance investigation could make them. They should assume that our powers are explosive, our conventions inexplicable, our reactions unforeseeable

and violent. . . . They may also assume with high probability that our viruses are deadly—a single sneeze from us might mean a Black Death pandemic for them—every one of their crews wiped out by our breath of death more effectively than by the most prodigious sky-defense barrage. No further proof is required to account for their preliminary caution.

What are we then to say about our present state of information in answer to the question, "What if anything is inside a saucer?" We have to follow the most difficult of mental disciplines, we have to keep an open mind. We have to take all the evidence and test its probability. Disks do exist. The weight of evidence is heavy enough to tip the scales in favor of that conviction. But as to who or what guides and maybe cruises in them all we can say is that it is not true to say there is no evidence that no one is inside and no one has ever been seen outside. Now that we know space travel is a possibility, the possibility of coming in touch with another form of life that is intelligent, and, we may hope, also already ahead of us in its knowledge and behavior, is far too promising a proposition for us to lose any chance of gaining more insight into so fascinating a mystery.

Left: Taormina, Sicily, 1954: Four Sicilians gaze skyward at two UFOs.

Right: Cluj, Romania, 9/1968: This photograph, taken by a tourist, shows an Unidentified Flying Object flying over Romanian territory.

Inset: Onomichi, Japan, 10/11/1974: This photograph was taken by a fifteen-year-old high school boy, Kazuhiko Fujimatsu, who claims to have seen a hat-shaped flying saucer near Hiroshima

Waking Up

These were my worst nights, 3 a.m., waking to claws ravaging the
       garbage cans outside the mortuary,
Squawk-bleat of cats in heat, perdition's spit and hiss, and then the
       rending down through plastic bags
To the scavenging at the very core of things, a fierce, liquid gnawing
       of gristle fevered occasionally by competition,
And then gone, leaving only the room smeared with the unction
       of streetlights, a cheap vinyl couch
And matching chair, the one fabulous child asleep, and the woman
       I did not love, sleeping also,
The ventilation of her snoring like those slubs or rips craftsmen leave
       in the fabric to suggest the virility of error,
And then the birds, the red, many-ventricled machine of their clarity,
       first the male and then the female
At the ancient ping-pong of shrill territorial claims and bland warblings
       of adoration, which served as both
Aubade and counterpoint to my guilt, my doomed, unnecessary,
       hydra-headed guilt.

All morning, Melody, the teenage welfare mother across the hall,
       would plot with her social worker to come off the dole.
Drunk by midafternoon, ranting to her colicky child, "Shut up,
       just shut the fuck up, you little pig!"
She flung her red spike heels against the wall to make the pre-Depression
       plaster fall. Over now and done—

Twilights I walked, with no choice but to walk, and left back there
      like eyeglasses on the counter of a grocery store
Where I had gone for milk, and when I came back, a hearse
      had backed up to the side door of the funeral home,
The wood of the casket shining, and under it, the unimaginable body,
      the human lettuce of autopsies—
Many nights I came back to the house, wanting another life, and
      climbed the stairs to the three brown rooms,
And there it was, stretched out before me, and by God it was my life,
      and still it was not my life.
The six black men bore down the gamut of last friendliness and slid
      into the hearse.

But how untrue *I* was, how craven, not to have spoken of it, only to have
      drifted off on the whim of some half-ass infatuation:
Body of the instant, high cheekbones, heavy legs, dark African-Caribbean
      eyes, each night, the breasts
I lifted like mugs, the mouth's wet kiss and Catholic cry, "Don't hold back,"
      and "Come inside of me."
Christ, stepping out on the path of wayward husbands, getting it
      on the side in the apartment of a friend—
And once, both of us drunk, crawling in the wrong window to find an
      old woman whispering to a scabby Pekingese dog.
Eyes pronating under the balding patch of skull, she trembled up like
      a lit match hollowed suddenly by the north wind. We ran.
What could we do but run? And laugh, as we ran past the living buildings,
      down the dead street,
And into the car, whistling off through the enormous, jasmine-scented
      night, darting between
The hills of the Holston River to finally light on the black leaf
      of a parking lot.

My worst nights, how incredible and flimsy you were, woven of all
      the brevities, as though the cremation to come
Were but one instant among the infinite years the gods we no longer
      believe in take to make love from human error,
Or as though the existing god were abandon and my life were another
      man's life that woke when I slept
And slept when I woke, until I heard the cats, and went over to the
      moonlight to see what was torn and mutilated.
I leaned out. I knew I wanted to live. But what was my life, coming
      into focus above the toothed nucleus of the shadow?
It would take another two months, backbiting, slander, every kindness
      vanished, lawyers talking to lawyers,
But just then, before the settlement, there were the cats, their snarls
      balanced against their mouthfuls of meat.
Whatever it was, horror and ignorance. It would be important to love
      beauty, whatever beauty is.
It would take years. It might have been the guts. It might have been
      the heart.

Born in Prison

If you're born in America with a black face, you're born in prison.

—Malcolm X

—From conversations with Jean Stein, July 1995.

JOMO DAVIS   We left Carolina when I was twelve years old, and we moved to Virginia where my father was trying to find a better job. He and my mother were both sharecroppers. At first, I went ahead with my father and I didn't really want to. He don't believe in affection, you know. When he wasn't drinking he was the quietest, most peaceful person you want to know; but once he started, you could see him change right in front of you. He had a lot of Indian in him and you could tell. My mom was thirteen when I was born, so me and her grew up together. She was my best friend in a sense. And I guess that's one of the reasons I have so much respect for women.

Charlie Joe was my first white friend. He was about the only white boy that had a hangout card in my neighborhood. He and I worked together at a filling station. And on the side, the boss had us hauling whiskey. Me and Charlie were the best drivers around. We would go to Elizabeth City, North Carolina and out the back way to Virginia Beach.

Jomo Davis, 1977.

We did this about ten times. But when we came back the last time, somebody had told on us and we got caught.

Well, you know how Virginia Beach was in 1961. It's still racist. Charlie had a separate lawyer—I think the people we worked for got him his lawyer. Mine was court-appointed. I was eighteen and I didn't have a lot of court experience then. They split our cases up for the sentencing, and on this particular day when I come down, thinking I'm going back home, they say, "One of y'all is going to jail and one of y'all is going to the Army." I get sentenced to five years. You know, looking at the way the trials go now, it don't even seem like I went through a whole trial. When I come out of the courthouse that day, there was Charlie getting on the Trailways bus to go join the Army. I was gone for eighteen months to Southampton prison before they gave me parole.

I was the only one in my family ever to go to prison and it was terrible. You went through thirty-something days where you don't get to communicate with your people; there was no phone calls out of prison. Then the first time we had mail call, they brought me a letter from my mom and I found out my letter was opened. I went back to the guard and I said, "This letter is from my mom. What the hell are you doing opening it?" I raised so much hell they put me in the hole. And the guy said, "What you here for?" I said, "I didn't do nothing. The guy that brought me my mail opened my mother's letter." He said, "Man, you don't get no mail in here unless they look at it first." I said, "Why ain't nobody told me that?" He said, "Well, man, now you're down here for seven days on bread and water." Only thing I could have in the hole during that time was a Bible and that letter. And I didn't want the Bible in there, but the guard played a little game with me. When he took out the tray, I used to throw the Bible back out the chuckhole. And every time I threw out one, he'd throw two in and close the chuckhole up. We went up to five Bibles.

So that's how prison started out for me. You've got to learn the rules from everybody else and after that I went and asked about everything. But prison was devastating to me that first time because it was the first time in my life I had been in anything my mom couldn't get me out of.

ELIZABETH GAYNES

I grew up in Hastings-on-Hudson, where my mom still lives. But after I finished college, I said, "This country sucks. I don't want any part of it. I'm going away and I'm never coming back." I went to Europe, then to Israel, got sick, and came home a year later, just in time for Woodstock. Then my father challenged me, "If this country is so bad, you should do something about it." And I said, "It's beyond repair. There is nothing I can do." But then he had me to lunch with a friend of his who was a lawyer at the Civil Liberties Union, and the guy talked about some of the litigation they were working on, and I decided to go to law school. It was great, but weird. There were only five women in the law school at Syracuse in 1969.

JOMO DAVIS

I went to New York about a year after I'd come out of jail in Virginia. I went to stay with one of my uncles in the Bronx. And I started getting into politics. I hadn't read a lot or nothing before I came up to New York, but I started going to rallies, meeting people, listening to what's going on in the country. And I started listening to Malcolm X. I think it was reading his autobiography that really changed my way of living. I started looking at the problems that black people have from Malcolm's view and learning about black history, then I looked at the injustice, you know. And I become connected with the Panthers. My given name was Cleveland McKinley Davis. But I took the name "Jomo" for Jomo Kenyatta, the leader of the Mau Mau uprising.

We would dress in the berets and the black jackets, and that made us targets for everybody—for the police and the reactionary whites. So we was walking one day in the Bronx and the police jumped on the two guys with me and beat them up, so naturally I got involved. The police beat the shit out of us, right, and then got backups and put us in jail. When we got to court, they gave me attempted robbery against a police officer. The officer was asked what I wanted to rob him of, and he said it was his watch. So they put me in the Bronx House of Detention. And in there, man, I met some of the wildest people in the world. The Puerto Ricans was already in gangs inside the jails. Whatever they wanted, they'd tell you to pull it off and give it up. So that's when I really became a Panther. They respected the Panthers because they were scared of them.

Then they moved me up to Auburn. And we had an incident in 1970: We wanted to celebrate Black Solidarity Day and the warden granted it. But on that day they took me down to the front office in the prison and locked me in, just to take me away from the group because I was a leader. And when everybody else found out that I wasn't coming back, they broke in and took me out. So we had the day. But after that day they took all the heads—the heads of the Panthers, the Young Lords, the Five Percenters, the Nation of Islam—up to Attica and put us in the box there, which come to be known as Housing Block Z.

We was kept in six-by-eight-foot cells, and the only way to deal with the box was to dream a lot. Naturally you have dreams about different things in your life, growing up and so forth, and you more or less fantasize about what you've done or want to do. I guess that's what keeps you sane. You had to read just in order to survive there. We weren't allowed to speak when we went through the halls and the guards would bang on the walls with their "nigger sticks"—which is what they called their clubs. And I used to get into trouble. One time I pierced my nose and I was written up for destroying state property. We were ordered out of Housing Block Z by federal court in the summer of '71, then in September, the Attica rebellion happened.

ELIZABETH GAYNES I hadn't actually gone to law school thinking I would do prison work. Then when the rebellion started, it just took over that part of the state. I'd been involved before that in a White Panthers case in Michigan—and I was working for a lawyer representing the inmates who'd been indicted after the rebellion at Auburn prison in 1970; so I volunteered to work on the Attica case too. My first three years as a lawyer were spent on that one case. And, by the way, prison conditions really did change to some significant degree because of the events at Attica. People saw that the bars were keeping people out as well as keeping people in. The whole world got to look inside a prison and it shifted things. Americans shooting at other Americans wasn't something we got to see all that often.

JOMO DAVIS My role during the rebellion was to guard the door and provide safe passage in and out of the prison for the observers, people like Kunstler, Commissioner Oswald, and the media, and to take food and water and blankets to the houses and the inmates in the yard. 'Cause we had a lot of crippled people out there, and we had a lot of people out there that was on medication. I got shot the first time when I was standing outside in the yard. The state troopers knew all the guys that was like so-called leaders, so they snipered us off. My friend Dalou was there and he pulled me inside. I was bleeding a lot while I was in the tunnel sitting with my back against the wall, and I guess I tripped out— I seen myself as a boy, in little pants and the shoes I hated.

When the troopers and correction officers came around after the rebellion and saw that I was still living, that's when they shot me through the neck and five times in the back. There was a lot of people who got shot then. We found out later that Rockefeller believed that if he made an example of the people here, there would be no more of these riots. And so they was trying to get rid of the guys that initially participated in it. Then they waited until the whole thing was over with and then came around picking people up. As a matter of fact, they put me in the dead pile. I tried to tell them that I was alive, but I couldn't talk because I'd been shot through the neck. So I just stayed there. With all the problems going on around me, I was glad to be out of that yard. Then about two hours later they came through checking the dead pile, and I grabbed the boot of a National Guardsman who walked past me.

So they took me from the morgue area and put me into a cell with my open wounds. I was just laying there on a stretcher on the floor, with water two or three inches deep. It was cold and the water might be what kept me from going into shock. The doctor came and pulled up the blanket and said, "There's nothing wrong with him." About twenty-four hours later, I was put in the hospital area. It worked against

Attica, September 13, 1971. The guards have retaken the prison.

me to be in the Panthers because they wouldn't take me to the outside hospital. The warden ordered me to be chained to the bed. I wasn't given no medication and they dealt with the wounds without anesthesia or anything. The state troopers sat outside my cell with a tripod shotgun the whole time. And it must have been days before anyone got clothes or anything like that. People stayed naked for a long time.

ELIZABETH GAYNES The lawyer representing the inmates who'd been charged at Auburn gave me a list of possible witnesses to interview. I went to three or four different prisons to see them, but nobody would talk to me. They said, "Well, I'm in the Panther Party and I can't speak to you unless our Minister of Defense tells me okay. So you need to talk to Jomo." Or they'd say, "Do you have a letter from Jomo saying I should talk to you?" Of course, after two weeks of this and five hundred miles of driving around upstate New York, I got pretty annoyed.

Jomo's name was already on my list so I went to see him. I said, "*Look*, I'm a law student, I'm trying to help, . . . will you please just . . . " And he thought it was hysterically funny. It was probably the first time

Attica, September 13, 1971. Prisoners are forced to strip and are reportedly beaten on their way back through "the gauntlet" into the prison.

he'd laughed in months. Then he said, "Well, tell me why you want to talk to them." I was prepared to have a forty-five-minute conversation and I was there for five hours. I went back the next day and talked to him for another six hours. I had no idea where the time went.

I called my parents that day and said, "The weirdest thing happened today. I met the man I'm going to marry." I wasn't even in love with him. I just had this idea, "Oh, this is it. There's some connection." It was very strange, because I certainly wasn't there looking for company. And he certainly wasn't going to admit to anybody that he was interested in me. He had this extremely militant language and had condemned any black man who would be seen near a white woman. But we started a correspondence. We actually wrote each other at least ten pages a day for years.

JOMO DAVIS   Up to that time I had never really talked to white women, and I didn't want to. I was racist myself, I guess, with the whole Panther thing. I was studying red books and black books and following Mao Tse-tung and

Elizabeth Gaynes, Syracuse, 1972.

everybody.... But I had my idea of what a woman I liked should be like, you know; a woman shouldn't just listen at me and shut up if I raise my voice. So Liz was sitting there raising all this hell, and I just started laughing. We had some arguments and all that, but I really got to like her 'cause she had a lot of fire. She reminded me of Janis Joplin. All them colors and tie-dye shirts and everything. Liz was a flower child. I was kind of scared of flower people at first because they was always related to LSD and Timothy Leary. But I got to like her.

You know, being a Panther, you have all these white girls—we used to think they was hippies—that would follow you like they do the musicians. I used to run away from 'em. But after I got to know Liz, she kind of changed my mind about it. Then I found out we was being stupid, too, because during that time we thought we could liberate everybody and we thought we could do it all ourselves. We found out we couldn't do that because the majority of the black people wasn't politically conscious. And not everybody white felt like the people that enslaved us. And I thought about how stupid it would be that you blamed the people today for the problem of four hundred years ago. So I had some problems with what all of them stood for. I said, "We're being more stupid than we say they are by doing this."

ELIZABETH GAYNES Jomo's mother died while he was incarcerated at Attica. There is nothing worse than losing a loved one while you're in prison and can't do anything about it, and can't even grieve in private. We had him transported to her funeral. We had to pay plane fares and hotel for him and a sergeant and a captain—I begged and borrowed from everybody I knew—but they did bring him down to North Carolina. His mother was one of twenty-one brothers and sisters and there were over four hundred people at the funeral. The sergeant had him in restraints, but when they got to the church, Jomo said, "I just don't feel I can go into a church with handcuffs on . . . I can't do this." So the sergeant said, "Do you promise me that you won't run?" And Jomo said, "I swear on my mother's grave I will not use her death to run." So they took the handcuffs off and let him walk through.

Later, when we were standing at the grave site, we suddenly heard a relative saying, "Who's that white woman up there with Cleveland?" And I thought, "It's all over." But one of his cousins, to her credit, turned around and said, "She was good enough for his mother, so she'd better be good enough for you."

JOMO DAVIS To learn that my mother had died of cancer, I mean, that was devastating. When I lost her, it was like I lost part of my life. I really wanted to see her when I was in prison. I felt like I needed to tell her that I was all right, that I wasn't hurt that bad at Attica. And when I didn't get to see her again I always felt like there were things she wanted to tell me, and that's probably why I started having dreams about her. I'd dream about her telling me things that I should do or shouldn't do. I was always very bashful with girls, and I would never go with nobody nowhere if she didn't approve of 'em. She took a big liking to Liz. She be telling Liz how to make sweet potato pie. And that's like a real sacred thing in the South, you know, because your mother passes down her ingredients.

Liz was in law school then, but she wanted to quit. I said. "You gonna finish law school because you gonna be my lawyer." And Liz said, "I can't be your lawyer. You need a *good* lawyer." But she was one of the lawyers at my trial. And she got a lot of the precedents set in New York State.

ELIZABETH GAYNES The lawyers fought indictments against sixty-two of "the Attica Brothers," including Jomo. He had five indictments charging him with everything but singing too loud in church. But eventually, when it came out what kind of prosecution it was, all the charges were dropped and he was

Jomo Davis, Wyoming County Court, following
Attica indictments, 1973.

pardoned by Governor Carey. But that took a couple of years, during
which I visited him several times a week. Then he got out and we got
married and lived relatively normally for a period of time.

When he moved in with me, he was the neatest person I'd ever
seen. When you're used to such a small confined area, everything has
to have a place. The other thing he always did after getting out of
prison was turn on the television and radio as soon as he got in the
house. I'd never seen anybody try to watch TV and listen to music at
the same time before, and I asked, "Isn't this sort of distracting?" "Well,
you know, prison is so noisy that the only way I can deal with it is to
have my own noise." I guess if you're trying to have some sense that
this is your world, you've got to choose what to do with it....

George Bernard Shaw said the problem is that to understand
imprisonment you have to understand freedom. The enlightened
corrections worker understands that people go to prison *as* punishment, not *for* punishment. But there are other people in the world who
think that, "Prison is no big thing. They get to be with their friends,

they watch television, they get three meals a day." These are people who've never been locked in a closet against their will. But the assumption is that the kind of people who go to prison have less need for personal space than the rest of us enlightened people.

I was basically a Red Diaper baby. I mean, my father was very progressive, a real Marxist-Capitalist, like many people of his generation. They raised me on the *Monthly Review* and I.F. Stone. And it's given me the freedom to do this kind of work. Jomo was really a test of their politics. I think that both my parents were much more disturbed about his lack of formal education than his color. He quit high school in ninth grade—he ended up getting his diploma in prison—because he was bored by it. And the schools were still segregated, so you can imagine what it was like. As for the prison thing, I don't know. Our daughter, Emani, said that my mother told her how horrified they were at the time, but I never knew it. I guess it was obvious to them given the kind of person I was that, if they didn't support me, they wouldn't have seen me again. In fact, both of them became extremely fond of him over the years, and they came to understand that book-learning wasn't all there was.

I was about eight months pregnant when Jomo was arrested again. We were living in Albany at the time and had come down to Hastings for the weekend because my grandmother, who was in a nursing home, wasn't doing well. On Saturday, Dalou, the man who had saved Jomo's life in Attica, called—Dalou had also been charged at Attica but had skipped bail; then even though the Attica Brothers were pardoned, he was convinced that they would still charge him for bail-jumping if he turned himself in—so Jomo went to meet Dalou and a friend of his. He hoped to convince Dalou to talk to a lawyer about turning himself in. And the next thing I know, it's three o'clock in the morning, and I get a call at my parents' house telling me to go to a hospital in Brooklyn.

Jomo, Dalou, and his friend had been stopped by the police on the street in Brooklyn. And a shoot-out started between the cops and Dalou and his friend, which left Dalou and two of the cops dead. Jomo was shot getting into his car. He drove off, but he lost so much blood that he passed out and crashed the car a few blocks away. The off-duty policemen who found him assumed he'd been involved in the shoot-out—even though he was unarmed. They handcuffed him to a stretcher in the ambulance and kicked and pistol-whipped him so badly that they broke his skull in twenty places and fractured the orbits around both eyes. The doctor testified later that if he didn't know better, he would have assumed that Jomo had fallen out of a five-story building.

When my parents and I got to the hospital, he was in police custody. First they told me he wasn't there; then they told me we couldn't talk to him; then they told me he didn't want to talk to us; then they told me that he was unconscious and couldn't talk to us; then they told me that he had been moved to another hospital. I would have believed them if they hadn't had to wheel him down a hallway ten feet from me. He was literally unrecognizable because of what they had done to his face—they performed massive amounts of reconstructive surgery later to cover that up—but when I saw his body going by on a gurney, I said, "Those are Jomo's feet." He has these really ugly, size-14 feet and I knew them right away. His face didn't look like anyone I knew. He still looks a little funny, actually.

When they interviewed the witnesses at the scene, the "perpetrator" who shot the cops was clearly identified as a 5'6" male Hispanic with a beard. Jomo is 6'3", black, and didn't have a beard. He was tried three times and then acquitted. The case hit the front page of *The New York Times*, *The Daily News*, and *The Post*. Two white cops dead. Black man arrested. It was a big mess. And I had friends who were so freaked out by the whole thing that they literally never spoke to me again.

Most of that time is a bit of a blur. I was completely in shock. After his arrest, Jomo's parole officer took the police into our apartment, tore the place up, then claimed to have found a shell casing of unknown origin and potentially explosive objects. I had to piece it together: In '77, we had bought some Fourth of July fire crackers—in some state that allows you to buy fireworks—and left them in my closet. Those were the "explosives." Then I remembered that when I'd been in Israel, I'd found some huge shell casings from the Six-Day War, that were apparently made in Russia, lying on the ground. I had several of them in my living room with flowers in them. They were seized and used by the press as evidence of our involvement in firearms. Our supposed Communist involvement was based on the fact that we had a leaflet in our car, that Jomo had picked up at some rally, that mentioned the PLO. By the time *that* got into the newspaper it was "PLO Link Suspected." For my aunt, the idea that Jomo was connected with the PLO was way worse than the idea that he could have killed a couple of cops.

EMANI DAVIS The other kids would ask me where my father was, or they would find out. It wasn't hard to find out, I guess. And a lot of my friends' mothers wouldn't let them play with me anymore because, I don't know, I was a bad influence or maybe I was dangerous. . . . I don't know what they thought, but I remember losing friends that way. And that's when I started to lie about where he was. I started to say, "Oh, he's working down South," or, "He's on a trip." I used to make up all kinds of stories. And it took a long time before I would tell even my closest friends where he was. We moved about seven times in fifteen years, and after a while I didn't really tell people about it anymore. And there was nothing that my mother could say to me to like make it all right. There was no explanation for why my friends couldn't be my friends anymore.

ELIZABETH GAYNES In a way, we were very lucky because it was such an obviously political thing, we really got a lot of support. The Black United Front in Brooklyn came to court. But it took over two years before Jomo was out of jail and I always felt that he stayed angry. I mean, it's infuriating to go through something like that, not being guilty. It permanently altered who he was. And he never got his eyesight back completely. He developed high blood pressure. He looked different and he'd lost two years

Jomo Davis, 1982.

of his life. He came out and I thought we had this really nice life. I had a great job in Washington and I didn't care if he got a job or not. It was okay with me if he didn't do anything but take care of Emani all day. I didn't appreciate his need to do something useful. He had trained as a barber in prison years before. And he had actually just completed the degree that he needed to go into the hairstyling business when he was arrested in Brooklyn. One of the things he liked about hairstyling was that it was a clean profession, as opposed to the mechanic jobs that his father had done. But by the time he got out, his vision wouldn't allow him to do the precision cutting. And he was worried that he'd put people off, looking like Frankenstein with all his scars. So he worked at a car dealership and felt like life had passed him by. And he was self-righteous about it. In the end, I got sick of it. I said, "Come on, give it a rest. You've got a great family. You've got me. I know you don't like the job you have. But this is your life." And I guess I felt that he owed me. I had moved nine times. I had spent every cent that we had ever saved paying the lawyer. I felt like I had done everything. This is not a good way to be in a relationship.

We argued all the time and at one point Emani stood up on a table and said, "I can't stand this anymore. One of you has to leave." It was so brilliant because she didn't blame anybody. It was just, "One of you has got to go." She was five years old. So we recognized that that much anger can just burn people up. I guess all of our relationship tricks were based on managing crisis, and we just didn't have good, normal communication skills. Eventually, about a year after our son, Ari, was born, we agreed to separate, and I came back to New York. Jomo had been out for two or three years when we separated. Then three months after I left, he was arrested again.

He had been married before, and he had older children, one of whose gold chain had been stolen from his things while he was playing basketball. So Jomo and two men he knew found out who did it, and went to the guy's house to demand the chain back. The guy was on drugs when they got there and he stabbed Jomo. One of the men with Jomo shot the guy, and Jomo ended up in prison for felony murder. He didn't have a gun and he didn't touch the guy, but the law is that if you're involved in the commission of a felony (like forcing your way into someone's house) and someone dies, even if he just has a heart attack, it's felony murder, which can earn you a life or death sentence in Virginia. Jomo was sentenced to 122 years.

I think part of the reason he got such a long sentence was that he didn't stick around and wait to be arrested. He made it to the hospital, where he was treated for the stabbing, and when they didn't catch him there, he took off. And he came to New York and stayed with us for a few days. When he found out they were looking for him, he told me he was going back to turn himself in, but I never really believed that he would. The children and I were under twenty-four-hour surveillance for a year while they looked for him—even though we had already separated. He was on the FBI's Ten Most Wanted list. Their reports said that he was very attached to his children, which he is, and they believed that he would eventually try to see them. So whenever my daughter had a ballet recital, the FBI was there; when we went to Disney World, the FBI was there; they never left us. They tapped our phone and our house—I later learned that all the pay phones in the entire neighborhood in Park Slope had pen registers on them in case I tried to use them to call him.

Somebody eventually turned him in and we think it was a relative of his. The reward money was only $10,000, but for some of his family it might as well have been a million. Jomo is pretty forgiving—he just says that some of his people don't have the life competency that I take for granted.

EMANI DAVIS   I didn't know who the FBI guys were, but it became so normal to me. They never tried to hurt me or anything, so I was never like afraid of them. I remember my mother being honest, explaining, you know, that because Daddy was underground, they had to watch us to see if we ever met up with him so that they could catch him. There were a lot of things that she was dishonest with me about, but that wasn't one of them. You know, like they kept a lot of stuff from me, her and my aunt and my grandmother and my grandfather. Maybe they felt that it was inappropriate for me to know. But it's made me less trusting of my family. Even now, like when my mother talks to me about my father's parole or something, I don't believe her. I was like six when they caught him. My mother had gotten a phone call and we were in her room. I started crying. I don't think I understood, but I knew that the cops wanted him bad and I thought they were going to hurt him.

ELIZABETH GAYNES   When Jomo first went underground, I thought, "How do I explain this to the children?" But I went to see a child psychiatrist, and he said, "Well, you have to understand that when one parent disappears, they're going to worry about you disappearing too." And he was right. My son was nicknamed "Velcro" for a year and a half because it was as if I had Velcro stuck to my leg. Then, when a parent goes to prison, there's the question of this person whom they know to be a good person who is in a place where you're supposed to go if you're bad. It's incredibly confusing to them, and they have to learn that you can be a bad citizen and a good parent.

Or they get angry, like Emani did when she hit adolescence. And she was right. I mean, even though we don't think that what Jomo did was so evil, it was incredibly stupid and thoughtless on his part. This is a grown man who's had experience in the criminal justice system and he thinks you go banging on some guy's door and demand your son's gold chain back. It's macho, arrogant crap. And I was pretty clear that I was not willing to have him deal with Emani by acting like he was a victim in this. Thank God he didn't try to defend himself, he just said, "You're right, it was really stupid." I mean, life is scary enough as it is for children without saying to them, "Well, I'm here 'cause I'm black," or, "I'm here 'cause I was in the wrong place at the wrong time," or, "I made a mistake." I mean, kids make mistakes every day, they're in the wrong place at the wrong time all the time, and a lot of them are black.

EMANI DAVIS   There was a time when I got very angry at him. To me it was like, how many times do you need to get in trouble before you realize that it's just not all right? We had been supportive. My mother had moved back and forth to be close to him, and to do what was best for us. She'd drive by herself with two kids all the way from Brooklyn to Virginia to visit him. And I felt that he must not have been thinking about me when he was out there doing what he was doing, getting into trouble. And if he wasn't thinking about me, did he really love me? It didn't make any sense to me, so I just got angry. It hurt him very badly. I know it did. I don't think there was much he could say; there was no explanation, and the "I'm sorry"'s wore thin. I think he just respected me and gave me my space.

ELIZABETH GAYNES   One of the things about the prison experience is that you get institutionalized in the space. And I think that's partly why Jomo has ended up back in prison. He's now at the Powhatan Correctional Center, the state farm in Virginia. But he's been in so many jails since he was caught. Mecklenburg was by far the worst experience. One time, Emani must have seen the death row inmates and asked who they were. She was nine by then. And the woman guard said, "Oh, those are the people we're gonna fry." And Emani said, "What do you mean, 'fry'?" And she said, "Well, if you're bad we put you in a chair and we tie things to you and then we turn up the electricity until you're cooked."

Another time at the prison in Manassas, we drove past the guards' shack and the door was open and on the wall you could see a huge Confederate flag and a big swastika. I complained to the Virginia Department of Corrections, "I'm not comfortable visiting a prison with my little black Jewish kids when the employees are hanging swastikas." And they said, "Well, it's in the guards' cabin. It's not like it's public." And I asked, "Is that state land?" They said, "Yes." And I said, "Do you think there's anything wrong with having guards who think it's fine to hang Nazi flags?" So the flag was taken down and I insisted that Jomo be transferred. I guess they realized that they would have a big problem on their hands if something happened to him or me after that.

EMANI DAVIS   I have a lot of appreciation that my mom didn't just decide that, "Well, this is not the type of father that I want for my children, and so they won't see him." She really stood by him and let us have a chance to have our dad. But me and my mother have had a very up-and-down relationship my whole life. When we were living in Brooklyn—from the time I was six till I was thirteen—my mom worked all the time, trying to keep our co-op and raise two kids by herself. That went on for a long time and by the time stuff kind of got more balanced, I had already decided that I wanted to raise myself. So when I was eleven I joined a gang. And the next year I moved to Junior High School 51 in Brooklyn, and I got into a lot of fights. And being that I'm Jomo's daughter, it didn't make it any better for me, because they all knew who I was. Then some of my friends got murdered—one of them was shot and died in my arms—and that was very hard for me. My mom didn't know and I was upset and I was angry; and I know that I should have just told her, but you feel that your mom should just like know when you're hurting and just protect you.

Jomo Davis, Ari Davis, Emani Davis, and Elizabeth Gaynes, Powhatan Correctional Center, 1993.

I've forgiven my father because I know that the only thing that keeps him sane in prison is his family, and especially his children. And he's needed us since he was arrested more than he'll ever need us in his life. So I just try to be supportive. Sometimes I wonder what would have happened if he'd stayed in North Carolina, but I don't know. He would have never met my mother, and part of who he is, all the like wonderful things about him today, have to do with everything he's gone through. And although like a lot of bad came out of Attica and all that other stuff, he wouldn't be who he is.

I've been waiting for, what, eleven years for him to come home. I'm like almost graduated from high school now, so it's not like I ask him when he's coming home anymore. I don't even get my hopes up. But my father and I are very close. Like, if he's sick, or if he's tired, he'll call me and I'll guarantee to be the same way. And that's actually helped me deal with him being away, 'cause ever since I was a little girl he used to tell me, "Don't be sad for me because I can't see the world out there, because I see the world through your eyes." And I've always believed that. Because the same way I trust God's word, I trust my father's word.

ELIZABETH GAYNES
Jomo's been in prison for ten years now and he's actually eligible for parole. But Governor Allen has abolished parole in Virginia, so I don't think it will happen real soon. Jomo's in his fifties now, which is geriatric in prison. There was a time when he was treated as the most dangerous man alive. But in Virginia he's a model prisoner. Prison is a society like any other. And in that society he has a high degree of respect and freedom. I mean, he is as close as you get in that world to being a star. He's made it safe for himself, which is important—he's an old man and some of these young kids are predators. And if he didn't have the right presence, they would want to take on someone like him. On the other hand, he is someone who understands freedom enough to know that he doesn't have it. And you can see it in his eyes—it's like the tiger at the zoo; he never stops looking for a way out.

Prison is just brutally boring and the more intellectually active a person is, the more deathly it can be. I remember Jomo called me once years ago, at the beginning of his time at Powhatan, and said, "You know, I haven't cried in a long time, but I cried last night." And I said, "Why?" And he said, "Well, this is gonna sound silly, but, you know, I once spent four months in the box for wanting to read *Soledad Brother* by George Jackson and I saw it here yesterday in the garbage. These kids have no idea. They have the right to read these things and they can't even read. I walk around with these bullets from Attica in my back. What the hell did I do this for?"

JOMO DAVIS
After Attica, the New York State Senate Crime Committee and all these other commissions, they interviewed all of us to try to find out what causes Atticas, why you have these riots and so forth. And one of the

things we found out in these interviews is that they allow a certain amount of drugs in prison. They do that all the way from the White House. When you get a very big population in prison, they'd rather have a certain amount of drugs to keep 'em quiet. You can easily tell a crackhead in prison because they have no talent for working. And most of these people can't read past, "Dick and Jane see Spot run." But if you listen in on their conversations, they got four Cadillacs, they got ten women. And now the prisons are filling up with these type of people. I don't know what they gonna do for 'em in the long run. These brains that they done killed with crack—and the part of the brain that's still left, it don't work from thinking; it's instinct, they function like dogs. They don't watch the news, they're not into sports . . . and this is strange to me, right, because sports are where you learn teamwork and where you learn the rules of life. They don't even understand the idea of rules.

EMANI DAVIS   My father's faith in the young brothers is kind of thin now and so is mine. I'm with them every day and I've dated a lot of them, and it's all about getting high and making money and seeing how many females you can sleep with or get pregnant. They have no role models anymore. Not rappers, not basketball players. Because they're out of the ghetto now, but the ghetto is still in them, and they will carry that with them forever.

ELIZABETH GAYNES   Jomo probably has more friends among correction officers than inmates now just by virtue of age. But I think he's lonely. And he hasn't accepted the possibility that he'll never be released. He says he doesn't care if he sees another person as long as he lives, he just wants to see grass and sky; he wants to farm and have space. I figure that he could probably survive another three or four years in prison. After that I think he is going to become a very bitter person. I think if he truly believed that he was never going to get out of prison, he would be in a very different mental state.

JOMO DAVIS   I never feared death. I learned in Attica when I almost died a couple times that death is not all that bad. When you go through the whole revolutionary thing, one of the first things you learn is that you're just one of a number of people. But I wouldn't wanna die in here. I don't think my spirit or soul would be at rest if I died in prison.

Newsstands

Newsstand #3, 1994.

Newsstand #22, 1994.

Newsstand #14, 1994.

Newsstand #16, 1994.

Newsstand #13, 1994.

Newsstand #1, 1994.

A major contradiction in the history of photography is that a discipline such as taxonomic photography, which often aims for the cool, distanced, and objective recording of architectural structures is invariably usurped by the sociological readings which steal into any analysis of these images.

Moyra Davey's photographs of newsstands in New York City in 1994 were taken with this disparity in mind. Like other anthropologically-influenced photographers, Davey attempts to capture and record the societies, objects, or structures which are assumed to be on an extinction list. Like photography itself—which is destined to be conditioned and transplaced by digitized imagery—the newsstands she has chronicled may mutate or lose their function, as news services become accessible from home on the information highway.

Yet any determinist notion that these ad hoc, urban structures are relics that properly belong to the last century, or are remnants of the Mechanical Age, ignores the culture behind them, the convenience, pleasure, and sustenance they provide—how they enliven the commuter's daily journey with such ephemera as lottery tickets, horoscopes, and racing forms, and provide relief for those in need of cigarettes, a snack, soda, or aspirin on the run. Foot-hold businesses—like taxi-driving or deli-groceries—generally run by immigrant groups, these newsstands and the life within them provide a mirror-image of the city's varied cultural configuration and an example, in miniature, of the ownership and monopoly structure of New York's commercial life.

These clear, detailed photographs don't put a gloss on the disorderly. Instead, they reinvigorate an objective style by exposing it to the quotidian.

—Jackie McAllister

The Memory of the City

A city and its myths are inextricably linked: What is Jerusalem if not the "mythical" center of the world? What is Alexandria without its Greek and Levantine myths? Can it be experienced without Cavafy or Durrell? What about New York? Rome? Paris? What is real about a place and what spawned from stories and histories?

Cities are invisible stories, and stories are invisible cities, to borrow Italo Calvino's words. Which is why I find talking about Beirut such a difficult task. Should I tell its history or should I unravel its myths? And what if those myths are still in the process of being generated today? Should I use Roland Barthes's mythological approach or should I dig deeper under the archaeological foundations of the city's historical memory?

Beirut today can be understood both as a mythological prototype of the city torn by civil war, disheveled by death, dismembered by destruction, and as a former Roman and Phoenician city, a city with a past built on ruins of the past. The two perspectives are not altogether different: in ancient history Beirut was demolished by seven earthquakes; in recent times, it has been razed by the seven major wars that punctuated its civil war. The city remains unstable, if temporarily sedated by the peace pact signed in 1989—which is, in itself, a myth the city may smother at birth.

•

The civil war's destruction was systematic and widespread, eventually reaching almost all the institutional structures of Lebanese society: In 1975, at the outset of the war, most of Lebanon's prisons were destroyed and their prisoners set free; by the end of 1976 no prisons were functioning at all. Beirut's most renowned jail, Habs el-Raml, was bulldozed. Its most important mental hospital, al-Asfourieyh, was shut down in 1976, after confrontations between its patients and resident staff. Since this hospital was located in Beirut's eastern Christian sector, many of its Moslem residents fled in chaos and under duress. The site now serves as a prison for mentally ill or drug-addicted convicts. Schools were also closed down during the first two years of the civil war. The educational system collapsed, and one of the city's most pressing imperatives is to rehabilitate it. During the war, cemeteries were raided, graves looted, collective burial grounds dug. The physical parameters that had separated the realms of the living and the dead disappeared. Public workers ceased to perform their duties, and garbage began to shape the streets and public spaces, often becoming a receptacle for dead bodies.

As the standard social parameters became first dysfunctional and then nonexistent, they were replaced by two new spaces in which the war-torn city could survive: First, residents took refuge in religious sectors, boundaries within the city between places of belonging and places of nonbelonging. These sectors were not immune to war, however, and each eventually broke down into ever-smaller sectors. Second, there was the face mask, usually a brown bag, which hid the identity of the fighter, the intruder, the kidnapper—and was later used to hide the faces of hostages.

The unbridled spaces of war: spaces which made daily life in Beirut a myth in itself. Survival was our leitmotif, our sole concern to safeguard body and soul, to recreate life in the midst of overwhelming horror and death. At the center of this, writing became a necessary means of survival. Naming the horror was a way to protect oneself from it.

Recently there has been much discussion in Beirut concerning the city's reconstruction. Plans have been drawn, experts summoned from all over the world, and maps drafted—maps delineating the "new city," a city that no longer resembles its old self, but is rather a modern financial center, a collage of other cities' fragments: Singapore, Manhattan, Hong Kong, and Paris.

The huge machine that is reconstructing and regenerating the city is already wiping out the memory of old Beirut, relentlessly tossing the rubble of the old city into the sea. The city's center, today, is an empty space, a placeless space, a hole in memory.

How are we to preserve the memory of this place in the face of such frightening architectural amnesia?

In this city systematically ravaged by civil war, the only space left for memory is literature. Indeed, in any attempt to analyze the destiny of a city's myth, it is crucial to understand the difference between the role of the architect and that of the novelist. Although both architects and novelists imagine places, cities, houses, and create them*, the architect's media are building blocks and construction materials and the writer's are symbols in language. The architect can, and is sometimes forced to, destroy what is anterior to his drawings in order to erect the new. The writer destroys nothing. Where an architect works to establish differences, organize relationships, and define limits, a writer works to tear down these limits, to transcend definitions, to open spaces onto one another. As literature tries to carve doorways between the declared and the undeclared, architecture seeks to hang the doors which come between them.

Literature and architecture are two sides of the same equation. The contradictions they carry are complementary. Now that the horror has dissipated, both have begun to redefine spaces and things. The memory of war is now being stored both in the physical environment and in the city's myths.

•

There are three possible approaches to the regeneration of an old city. The first entails the partial (but not total) destruction of the old city to make way for the new. The Ottoman governor of Beirut, Azmi Bey, adopted this approach, in 1915, when he formulated plans to destroy huge quarters of the city. His efforts were cut short by the defeat of the Ottomans in World War I, and were then aborted by the French Mandate which ruled Lebanon and Syria until 1943. (The French Mandate, in turn, rebuilt Beirut, wiping out traces of the Ottoman City and extending the shoreline by building landfills with the rubble of Ottoman landmarks.)

---

* The Arabic word for a unit of poetic verse, *al-Bayt*, also means *house*.

The second approach creates a new city to surround the old one— a classical attempt to create clearly defined boundaries between the pre-colonial and the established colonial city, mutating the pre-existing into a ghetto or folkloric site. French colonial rule took this approach in Algiers. So did Israeli planners when they rebuilt cities whose inhabitants were not forcibly expelled during the war of 1948—and again in Nazareth, Acre, and now in East Jerusalem. The Israeli government's urban regulations in Acre, for example, prohibit its inhabitants from renovating or rehabilitating their houses, thus encouraging them to leave the central city. Acre will eventually become a ghost town, an agglomeration of vestiges, to be photographed by tourists.

The third approach is to destroy the city's existing fabric entirely in order to build a new "modern" city. This is unfortunately the path that the present Lebanese government has chosen for the regeneration of Beirut.

In his book *Torture in Islam*, the Iraqi writer Hadi al-Alawi defined the prisoner as someone who is "outside life," neither dead nor alive, living in a grave. Given the polemics of reconstruction and deconstruction that the city's architects and urban designers have introduced, Beirut may return, not as a city, but as a jail.

Beirut's original dump was in the eastern suburb of the city—the "Quarantina" or "quarantine" quarter. The city's slaughterhouses and hospitals for contagious diseases also occupied this quarter—a segregation that provided citizens with triple protection from hygienic hazards. At the outset of the war, however, the western Moslem sector was cut off from this site and was forced to create its own dump. The Normandy bay, at the foot of the deserted Normandy and Hilton hotels where the city center hits the shoreline, was chosen as the new site.

Today, there is an empty, silent space where the heart of Beirut used to be. The plans for the new city called for the severely damaged remains of the old city to be wiped out and that rubble has served to extend the area of the dump to create a solid buttress for the garbage landfill in the sea. Emptiness feeding a dump: recycling is the logic of the regenerated city. The dump today is a series of small putrefying hills, seething with tiny volcanoes that eject methane gas into the city's atmosphere.

Three projects have been drafted for its rehabilitation: The first, proposed by the French company A.P.U.R. in 1978, suggests transforming the dump into a public garden. The second, proposed by a company owned by the Prime Minister Rafik Hariri, Solidère (Société Libanaise pour le Developpement et la Reconstruction du Centre Ville), in 1991, recommends moving the dump to form an island offshore, building skyscrapers on it, and turning it into a major financial center. Another Solidère idea, proposed in 1993, was to turn the dump into a prolongation of Beirut's shoreline, which would house both a financial center and a public park. With the dump at the center of redevelopment talks, the reconstruction process is unavoidably linked to the issue of recycling. The old city has been recycled and reformed to create the new one.

During the civil war, according to a 1995 Greenpeace report, 15,800 barrels and twenty containers of toxic chemical waste were imported from Italy and buried in Lebanese soil. A minor percentage of the waste was returned to Italy after it was publicly revealed, in 1988, that several Lebanese businesses were importing and burying the waste, but the major part remains scattered across the country (despite the Italian government's claims to the contrary). Dozens of barrels that turned up in the northeastern mountains surrounding Beirut were collected and stored in the port at the edge of the dump. Some of these hazardous wastes, which contain water-soluble compounds potentially lethal to fauna, flora, and humans, were dumped in the sea just outside the Beirut harbor. In some cases, barrels that had contained the wastes were distributed to villagers for use as food storage bins and water tanks....

While Beirut attempts to regenerate itself by recycling garbage and destroying its own memories, it imports waste that it will never be able to recycle. As it struggles to rebuild its physical environment as a modern, international financial center, it has degenerated into just another dump in the larger industrial waste receptacle which was once known as the Third World.

•

In the midst of these contradictions, what myths remain? The reconstruction project provided an incredible opportunity for archaeologists to uncover Beirut's ancient foundations: the Roman Law School, the Roman city-state Berytus, the Byzantine mosaics, the Phoenician city....Ancient edifices, witnesses to a distant past, were cloistered by fences, contiguous to the new strange, modern structures, witnesses of the future-to-be. Between the two, all traces of recent past and present time have been eradicated. The present—the civil war and its remembrance—plays no role in the regenerated myth. The buildings of Beirut which used to weave an urban fabric inscribed in history and to embody its continuation, are gone.

Beirut is a dim shadow, an environment shaped not by social interaction, but by private real estate speculators. Its inhabitants are marginalized, removed from the decisions that will shape their lives. The eradication of current memory has led to a breakdown in the relationship between culture and the lived experience. Culture is a mere tool for marginalization and oppression, propagated through the media. It serves as a veil between the individual and his image. When culture ceases to represent the present time, it becomes a source not of enlightenment, but of debilitation.

Current polemics about the reconstruction of Beirut do not pit regression and nostalgia for the old city against progress and the bulldozers that are clearing the way for modernity and technology; rather, the issue requires that we understand the importance of acknowledging and shaping our present time.

Both the novelist and the architect sculpt the relationship between a space and its living memory. Intellectual recycling in Beirut has not only burned holes in its citizens' memories, it has also erected a barrier between the individual and his physical environment. It has created fertile ground in which military and psychological dictatorship can take root.

When the individual is unable to identify with his present and his past, when his physical realm is obliterated and his ownership stripped away, when the culture of representation becomes a culture of consumption, then this recycling of the city is one more element in a global move toward impoverishment, domination, and destruction.

After Fires

In the time when they were still burning witches and
    the word of the king meant little in the mountains
and tribunals were dispatched into the outlying
    darkness with power to administer the law
on the spot a woman was brought in one day accused
    of burning down two or three houses and perhaps more
as the courtiers were given to understand
    that this was customary in the region when
someone had been displeased and when the snow was upon them
    then they set their fires but the setting was hard to prove
for the fires were plotted in secret and set at night
    and when it was said that she had been seen leaving
her house after dark carrying fire and later
    that night a house had burned she denied any part in it
and the witness was muddled and useless and although
    it was plain that this was a woman of unsavory
character who had produced several children without
    being married which she said was the men's doing
when she was condemned to the question a matter
    in that place of nothing more than a violent
stretching she bore it with firmness and confessed nothing
    saying only that the judge hoped for a reason
for hanging her and so at last she was branded
    with the lily and banished to burn some said other houses
and beget other offspring I thought of her long after
    she had gone like smoke and after those courts were dust
and after the time when everyone stopped in the middle
    of the noon meal in a moment of autumn sunlight

and suddenly we were running up the white road
    toward the column of dark smoke rising out of itself
swelling and unfurling into the blue sky over
    the ridge we were halfway there before the first bells
rang behind us too late too late and when we came in sight
    the neighbors had carried out the old woman and set her
on a mattress on the ground she was not even watching
    the neighbors throwing their buckets of water and
her son dragging out one smoking thing after another
    none of them what he wanted he had not been there
when it began and nobody knew how it started
    everyone informed everyone as the fire truck
finally got there and the hoses began unrolling
    then the firemen and the son were sorting through the hissing
remnants and the fallen stones trying to find a box
    as everyone told everyone and the old woman
said yes there was the box they should look for the box
    it was all in the box the papers and the money and they
peered under the rubble with the smoke still
    threading upward from the charred ends of the rafters
she said the box was made of iron it was under the stairs
    which were no longer there they found it at last the iron
too hot to touch and they wet it down and took it
    to the old woman who nodded but then they were
some time getting it open since the key was lost and the hoses
    went on playing the rest of the tank of water
onto the ruins through the glass dome of the afternoon
    and the ring of bodies was hushed around the mattress
when the son pried the lid off so that we could all see
    that there was nothing inside but a drift of black snow

The Cisterns

At intervals across the crumpled barrens
    where brambles and sloes are leading back the shy oaks
to touch the fallen roofs there under the flat stones
    note by note a covered music is staring upward
into the darkness and listening for the rest of it
    after a long time lying in the deep stone without
moving and without breath and without forgetting
    in that unmeasured silence the least of the sounds
remembered by water since the beginning
    whir of being carried in clouds sigh of falling
chatter of stream thunders crashes the rush of echoes
    and the echoes of drops falling from stones in the dark
moment by moment and the echoes of voices
    of cows calling and the whispers of straw and the cries
of each throat echoing over the one still note
    of the water and the echoes sinking in their time
into the memory of the water the notes
    one here one there of an art no longer practised

The Dream,
the Sphinx, and the
Death of T.

T errified, I noticed an enormous furry brown spider suspended over the foot of my bed, clinging to a thread that descended from a web right over the bolster. "No, no!" I cried, "I can't possibly spend the night with a threat like that over my head, kill it, kill it"—though the idea of killing it myself, whether in a dream or awake, totally revolted me.

At that moment I dreamed that I woke up, but actually my dream continued. I was in the same place on the bed, and at the very moment that I was telling myself, "It was only a dream," yet instinctively looking for the spider, I caught sight of something splayed out on a heap of earth and bits of broken plate or small flat stones—it was a yellow, ivory-yellow, spider, far more monstrous than the first one but smooth, apparently covered in smooth yellow scales, and with long thin legs that looked as smooth and hard as bones. Petrified, I saw my girlfriend's hand reach out and touch the spider's scales; she seemed neither frightened nor surprised. I screamed, and pushed her hand away, and then, just as I had done in the dream, I begged for it to be killed. Someone whom I hadn't yet seen crushed it with a long stick or shovel, beating it violently. I averted my eyes and heard its scales crack and the strange sound of the soft parts of its body being squashed. It was only afterward, when I looked at the remains of the spider lying on a plate, that I read a name written very clearly in ink on one of its scales; it was the name of a species of arachnids, a name that now escapes me. I've forgotten it, all I can see now are the detached letters, the black color of the ink on the ivory-yellow, the sort of letters you see on stones and shells in museums. It was quite obvious that I was responsible for the death of a rare specimen belonging to the collection of the friends whose house I was staying in at the time. This was confirmed a moment later by the lamentations of an old housekeeper who came in looking for the lost spider. My first impulse was to tell her what had happened, but I could foresee the trouble that would cause and how angry my friends would be with me: I ought to have seen that it was a rare creature, read its name, and told them about it instead of killing it. So I decided to say nothing, to pretend I knew nothing about it, and to hide its remains. I went out into the garden with the plate and crossed it taking good care not to be seen—the plate in my hands might seem strange. I came to a bit of ground that had been dug up and was hidden at the bottom of a bank by a thicket, threw the remains into a hole, covered it with earth, and trampled it down, saying to myself: "The scales will rot before anyone can discover them." At the same moment I saw my host and his daughter on horseback, riding past me on the bank above. They didn't stop, but said something to me that surprised me, and I woke up.

All of the following day I could see that spider; it obsessed me.

The day before, late at night, I had seen some ivory-yellow traces of pus on a glossy white sheet of paper and realized that I had caught the illness I had been expecting for a few days. Observing this, I was a little worried by the apparently involuntary mental paralysis that had prevented me from forestalling the threat of the disease, which I could easily have done, but which I hadn't bothered about. I had no reason to believe that this was a kind of self-punishment; it was rather that I had obscurely felt that the disease might be useful to me, might give me certain advantages, although I didn't know of what sort.

In bed that evening, and not long before the dream, my girlfriend had laughingly wanted to observe the symptoms of the disease.

I had been expecting to develop it since the previous Saturday. I had heard that the brothel called "The Sphinx" was going to be closed down for good, so at six in the evening I rushed off there, not being able to bear the idea of never again seeing that room in which I had spent so many hours, so many evenings, ever since it opened, and which I considered the most marvelous place in the world.

Going there for that last time, I was a little drunk, after lunch with some friends. One of the incidental remarks made at this lunch was that it would be interesting to keep a diary from day to day, and we discussed everything that might stand in the way of doing so. My first thought, which surprised me, was that I couldn't wait to begin such a diary, starting at that very moment, and in this connection Skira, to whom I had previously told the story of the death of T., asked me to write about it for the forthcoming issue of *Labyrinthe*. I promised him that I would, although I couldn't really see how it would be possible.

But since the dream, since the illness—which brought me back to that lunch—T.'s death had again become present in my mind.

That afternoon, on my way back from the doctor's, I wondered whether the fact that Skira's suggestion more or less coincided with my visit to The Sphinx, and all its consequences, was enough to bring back the memory of T.'s death and make me want to write about it now. Here I must mention that the pharmacy was on the Avenue Junot, practically next door to my doctor's house, and that as I was coming out of the store, carrying my tubes of Thiayzomides, the first thing that caught my eye was the name of the little café opposite: "Au Rêve" ("The Dream").

Walking home, I saw T., in the days before his death, in the room next to mine in the little house where we lived at the bottom of a somewhat neglected garden. I saw him in his bed, not moving, his skin ivory-yellow, his body huddled up and already strangely far away. Then I saw him shortly afterward, at three in the morning, dead, his skeletal limbs flung outward, spread-eagled, abandoned, his enormous swollen belly, his head thrown back, his mouth open. Never had any corpse seemed to me so nonexistent, pathetic remains to be tossed into the gutter like a dead cat. Standing motionless by the bed, I looked at his head which had become an object, a little box, measurable and insignificant. At that moment a fly approached the black hole of his mouth and slowly disappeared into it.

I helped to dress T. as smartly as possible, as if he had to make an appearance among the elite, at a reception, perhaps, or as if he were going on a long journey. Raising, lowering, moving his head as I would any nondescript object, I put a tie on him. He was strangely dressed; everything seemed to be normal and natural, but his shirt was sewn up at the collar, and he had neither belt nor suspenders, and no shoes. We covered him with a sheet and I went back to work until the morning.

When I entered my room the next night, I noticed that, oddly enough, there was no light. Invisible in the bed, A. was asleep. The corpse was still in the next room. I was oppressed by the lack of light, and I was just about to walk naked through the corridor leading to the bathroom which passed the dead man's room, when I was suddenly overwhelmed by panic and, even though I didn't believe it, I had the vague impression that T. was everywhere, everywhere except in the wretched corpse on the bed, the corpse that had seemed so nonexistent. T. had become infinite and, terrified that I might feel an icy hand touch my arm, it was only with an immense effort that I was able to go down the corridor. Then I went back to bed and, with my eyes open, talked to A. until dawn.

I had just experienced, in reverse, what I had felt a few months earlier about living people. At that time I was beginning to see heads in the void, in the space surrounding them. The first time I became aware that as I looked at a head it became fixed, immobilized forever in that single instant, I trembled with fear as I had never trembled in my whole life, and a cold sweat ran down my back. I was no longer looking at a living head but at an object, just as I might look at any other object. But, no, it was different; I wasn't looking at it as if it were any other object, but as if it were something alive and dead at the same time. I screamed in terror, as if I had just crossed a threshold, as if I were entering a totally unknown world. All the living were dead, and this vision kept recurring, in the Métro, in the street, in a restaurant, with my friends. There was a waiter at the Brasserie Lipp who froze, leaning over me with his mouth open, without the slightest connection with the preceding moment, or the following moment, his mouth open, his eyes staring in total immobility. And at the same time that men underwent a transformation, so did objects: tables, chairs, clothes, the street, even trees and landscapes.

When I woke up that morning I saw my towel for the first time; it had become weightless, in a stillness I had never yet known, and seemed to be suspended in a dreadful silence. It no longer had any relation to the seatless chair or to the table whose feet no longer rested on the floor, barely touching it; there was no longer any relation between these objects, which were now separated by infinite chasms of emptiness. I looked at my room in dread, and a cold sweat ran down my back.

A few days after having written the above text in one sitting, I felt I wanted to go back to it and revise it. I was in a café on the Boulevard Barbès-Rochechouart, where the prostitutes have strange legs, long, slim, and tapered.

A feeling of boredom and hostility prevented me from rereading it, and in spite of myself I began by telling the dream differently. I tried to describe the elements that had particularly affected me in a more precise and striking manner: for instance, the volume and bulk of the brown spider, the density of its hairs which seemed as if they ought to be agreeable to the touch, the position and exact shape of the outspread web, the expected and feared appearance of the yellow spider, especially the shape of its scales, their resemblance to flat, rippling waves, the strange mixture of its head, and the angles of its right front leg. But I wanted to convey all this in a purely emotional way, and make some parts of the description hallucinatory, without looking for the connection between them.

I stopped, discouraged, after a few lines.

Some black soldiers were passing by outside in the fog, the fog that had given me such pleasure the day before.

There was a contradiction between using emotional terms to convey what had hallucinated me, and the sequence of events I wanted to describe. I was faced with a confused mass of times, events, places, and sensations.

I tried to find a possible solution.

At first I tried to represent each fact by a couple of words which I placed in a vertical column on the page, but this didn't work. Then I tried to draw little compartments, also vertically, which I would gradually fill in so as to get all the facts on the same page simultaneously. But the time factor troubled me, so I tried to find a way to convey the whole thing chronologically. I kept coming up against the backward and forward movement of the narrative, though, and this worried me. Throughout my story, time went backward, from the present to the past, but it also returned, and had ramifications. In the original draft, for example, I hadn't been able to find a place to insert the episode of the Saturday lunch with R.M. before I went to the doctor's.

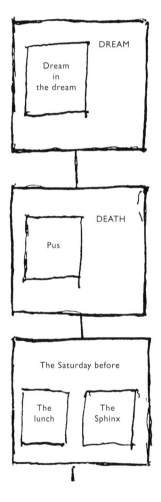

I had told my dream to R.M., but when I got to the part about burying the remains I saw myself in a different field, which was surrounded by thickets at the edge of a forest. Shaking the snow off my feet, digging in the rock-hard earth, I was burying a piece of bread that I had hardly even got my teeth into (theft of bread in my childhood), and I saw myself running through Venice, my hand clenched over a bit of bread that I wanted to get rid of. I crossed Venice looking for isolated districts and in one of them, after several unsuccessful attempts on the most obscure little bridges over the gloomiest of canals, finally, trembling nervously, I threw the bread into the stinking water of the most remote branch of the canal, enclosed within black walls, and I ran away, still in a state of panic and barely conscious of myself. This led me to want to describe the state I was in at that moment. And also to describe my journey to the Tyrol, Van M.'s death, see note, (that long, rainy day when I sat alone next to a bed in a hotel room, a book by Maupassant on Flaubert in my hand) as I watched Van M.'s head transform (his nose becoming more and more accentuated, his cheeks hollow, his almost motionless mouth barely breathing and, toward evening, as I was attempting to sketch his profile, I was suddenly terrified that he was going to die); and my stay in Rome the previous summer (the newspaper I saw by chance which contained an advertisement inquiring about my whereabouts), the train to Pompeii, the temple at Paestum.

But also to describe the scale of the temple, and that of the man who appears between its columns. (The man between the columns becomes gigantic, but the temple doesn't get any smaller; actual size no longer plays any part—the opposite of what happens at Saint Peter's in Rome, for example. The empty interior of that church seems small—especially in photographs—but the men look like ants. Saint Peter's doesn't get any bigger; it is all a question of scale.)

This led to a discussion of the scale of heads, and of objects, and of the affinities and differences between objects and human beings, and I ended up talking about what was foremost in my mind at the very moment that I was telling this story at that Saturday lunch.

Sitting in the café in the Boulevard Barbès-Rochechouart, I was thinking of all this and trying to find a way of expressing it. Suddenly, I had the feeling that all these events existed simultaneously around me. Time was becoming horizontal and circular, it was both time and space, and I tried to draw it.

Shortly afterward, I left the café.

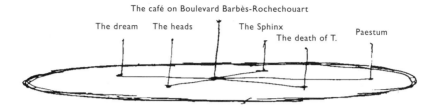

The café on Boulevard Barbès-Rochechouart

The dream   The heads   The Sphinx   Paestum
The death of T.

This horizontal disk delighted me, and as I walked along I saw it almost simultaneously under two different aspects. I saw it drawn vertically on a page.

The night
The curiosity
of A.

The trace of pus
on the glossy white
paper
The Sphinx

The Saturday lunch

The dream
The yellow spider
The lunch with R.M.
The buried bread
Venice

The dream in
the dream
The café on
Boulevard Barbès-Rochechouart
The bread in the canal
Van M.'s death
Paestum

The objects
The motionless towel

The visit to the doctor
"The Dream"

The heads immobilized
in the void

The death of T.
The corpse spread out
The corpse clothed
The dark corridor

But horizontality was what I was after, I didn't want to lose it, and I saw the disk become an object.

It was a disk about two meters in radius and divided by lines into sections. On each section was written the name, date, and location of the event it corresponded to, and on the circumference of the circle there was a panel facing each section. These panels were of different widths, and separated by empty spaces.

The story corresponding to each section was written on each panel. It gave me a strange kind of pleasure to see myself walking on this time-space disk, reading the story written on the panel in front of me. I was free to start wherever I liked, to start, for example, from the October 1946 dream and end, after walking the whole way round, a few months earlier, in front of the objects, in front of my towel. I was very anxious to get each fact on the disk in its proper position.

But the panels still have nothing on them; I don't know enough about the value of words or their mutual relationship to be able to fill them in.

Note: This journey on which I embarked in 1921 (the death of Van M. and the events that surrounded it) was something like a gap in my life. Everything changed, and the journey obsessed me continually for a year. I never stopped talking about it, and I often wanted to write about it, but was never able to. Only today, because of the dream and the bread in the canal, has it become possible for me to write it for the first time.

—Alberto Giacometti

Translated from the French by Barbara Wright

All Parallels Converge At Infinity

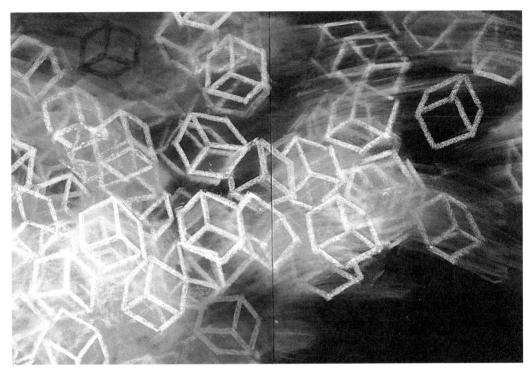

Onset of Turbulence (5), 1989.

Vanishing Point: Critical Mass, 1990–91.

Vanishing Point: Flash Forward, 1991.

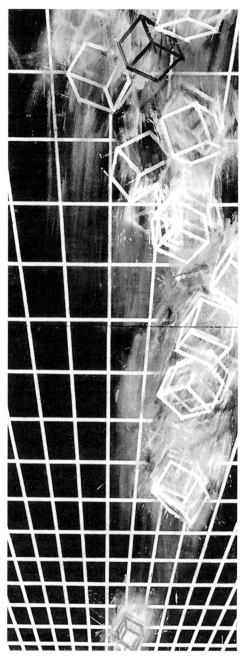

Vanishing Point: Vertical Drop, 1991.

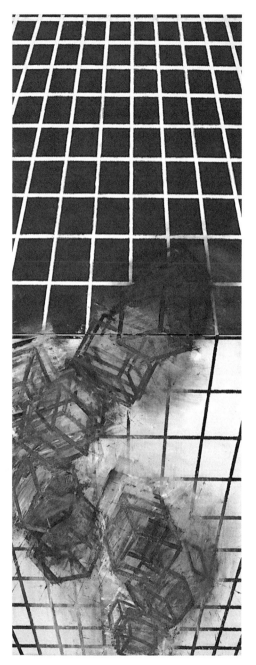

Vanishing Point: Sinking, 1991.

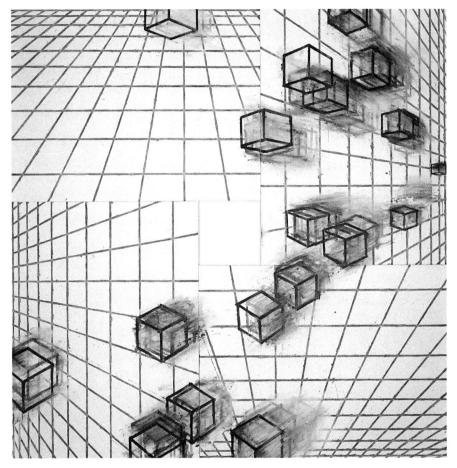

If At Every Moment The Arrow Is At Rest, When Does It Move?, 1992.

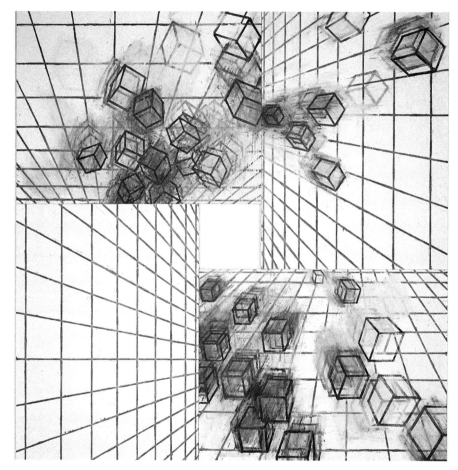

All Parallels Converge At Infinity, 1992.

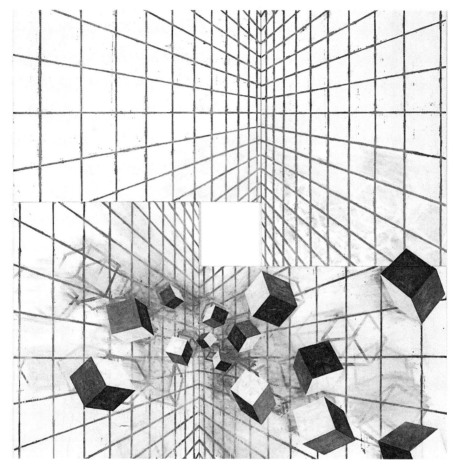

Unlived Time, 1992–93.

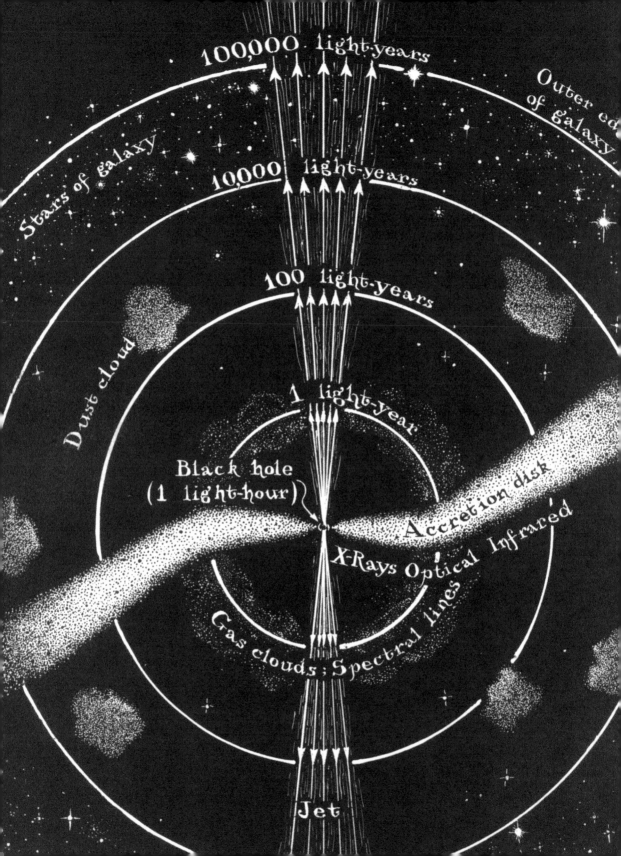

Ants on a Balloon

Kip S. Thorne is the Feynman Professor of Theoretical Physics at the California Institute of Technology in Pasadena, and is the author of the prize-winning book Black Holes and Time Warps: Einstein's Outrageous Legacy. *Jane Kramer met with Thorne in Pasadena in March 1995 to discuss the physicist's perception of space in the universe.*

JANE KRAMER: In the hypothetical voyage through space you describe in your book, you talk about arriving at a distance of ten percent to the edge of the known universe. Are you tempted by the edge of that space? Do you even conceive of it spatially?

KIP S. THORNE: We conceive of it, and we can infer to some modest extent what's beyond, but we see no sign at all that things will be any different beyond the edge of our known universe than they are right here. What we guess is that it just goes on and on, looking roughly like what we see in the parts of the universe that we can explore with our telescopes. If we wait another ten billion years, light will reach us from there, and we'll see what's out there.

JK: And beyond the universe?

KT: There is no beyond. We are like ants living on the surface of an expanding balloon. Except that the only part of that balloon that has any physical reality is its surface. The interior and exterior are just imaginary constructs—we call them hyperspace—to help us understand the surface on which we live. You might think that when we journey out over the surface—through the space of our universe—we will inevitably travel around the balloon and come back to where we started. But there hasn't been enough time since the birth of the universe, since this balloon began expanding, for us to get all the way around. We have no reason to believe that any part of the balloon that we can't yet see is any different than the parts that we can see.

So there is no beyond, no hyperspace; all that really exists is the three-dimensional surface of the balloon that we live on. Now, that's not entirely fair; there may well be other universes like our own, other balloons; and there may be connections between them, or there may have been connections between them when the Big Bang first created the universe, but if there are other universes, then those connections are so extremely weak that we have not seen any evidence of them.

JK: Can we, then, talk about a space between universes?

KT: Well, there really is no hyperspace between them, no "super-universe" in which these balloons live. The surfaces of the balloons might be connected by tiny threads, but the super-universe, or hyperspace, through which those threads reach, is just a figment of our imagination—in the sense that there would be no way for us ever to make measurements that would reveal it.

If you take a logical positivist point of view, it doesn't exist. But we physicists don't always take that view, because dealing with unmeasurable abstractions can often help us to make deductions about things that can be measured. We invent constructs that we know don't correspond to reality—as tools for intuition. I think in terms of hyperspace all the time, and it helps me to imagine black holes and multiple universes and so forth. But if anybody says, "Okay, I want to see this hyperspace," I have to tell them, "No hope."

JK: Are these the parameters that keep physicists from megalomania?

KT: I'm not sure that we all avoid megalomania. I'd like to think I do. I mean, I think almost all of us recognize that issues of theology are by and large beyond our ken, and we restrict ourselves to dealing with things that, in principle if not in practice, can be touched, heard, smelled, felt, and probed by instruments that we can build—which includes black holes, our warped universe, and information about the universe's origin, but not many of the issues that theologians are concerned about.

JK: One hears all the time about great scientists who become deeply religious at a certain point.

KT: There are a few that do that, but very few. I'm fundamentally an atheist, but I see no necessary conflict between religion and science. I just find religion rather a dull subject because you can't get definitive answers. I grew up a Mormon and I've had my days of theology, albeit a simple-minded version. I've had my fill of it, since it seems not to lead anywhere that you can test experimentally.

JK: Then your science was in some way instrumental to your leaving the church?

KT: I don't think so. What was really instrumental to my leaving the Mormon Church was its discrimination against women. My mother, Alison—who was about seventy-five at the time—wrote a letter to all her children, saying, "I've decided it's time for us to be excommunicated," and we all quite happily signed on. One of my sisters, Barrie, had already been excommunicated for her feminist activities.

JK: So your idea of space, both visually and theoretically, is quite concrete?

KT: Emotions are very tied up in our work, as are aesthetics, but warped space is as concrete as the table my arm is resting on. I think that people who aren't engaged in this enterprise think of it in mystical and metaphysical terms because they don't have the tools to make it concrete.

JK: And when you imagine, you imagine concretely?

KT: If you look at *Black Holes and Time Warps*, you'll see diagrams of warped surfaces and curves winding around in corkscrew ways amidst these fluted surfaces. That's what goes on in my mind when I think about the curvature of the universe, and the warpage of space and time inside black holes. When I'm trying to figure out what the sun would look like if I were sitting inside a wormhole (a hypothetical tube through hyperspace connecting distant parts of the universe), which is what I happened to be thinking about this morning, I think in terms of pictures, in terms of light rays traveling around and around in a corkscrew manner down the wormhole. I can sort of guess what the answer ought to be just by manipulating in my mind the images of these light rays traveling from the sun into and down this wormhole. Then I take pen to paper and work out the answer mathematically, based on the laws of physics. Typically, I find that my pictures missed some crucial facet, but I also find that the intuition that came from these pictures helped me choose the direction in which to calculate. And behind those pictures, there is a very concrete mathematics and there are the very physical laws that friends of mine can test with enormous precision.

My friends are building a set of large instruments, called the Laser Interferometer Gravitational-Wave Observatory or LIGO, to look at the ripples of warpage in space and time produced when black holes collide. LIGO will turn space-warp physics into a true experimental science. Its instruments will enable us to receive waves produced by cataclysmic space-warp events in the distant universe, waves that consist of tiny ripples of warpage in the fabric of space and time. These waves will carry information in much the same way that a symphony does, information that can be used to reconstruct pictures of the cosmic space-warp events that caused them. In this way, we can probe the part of the universe that does not emit light or radio waves or gamma rays—the "dark side" of the universe.

Take, for example, the collision of two black holes: We have no observational, experimental evidence of the properties of black holes, but we know that they make these gravitational waves, these ripples in space and time. In the distant universe, there should be pairs of black holes orbiting around each other, spiraling together, that collide and produce a cataclysmic burst of waves that travel out through the universe. By studying these waves, we can expect to reconstruct a map of the space warpage and time warpage within and around the black holes, and to test the theoretical notions that we have deduced about how they ought to behave as well as learning new features of their behavior that we haven't been clever enough to deduce from the laws.

JK: Does all the evidence suggest that black holes exist?

KT: We're essentially sure they exist, but we have no experimental evidence of their properties. We have observed stars orbiting around very dark, heavy bodies that we guess are black holes. Sometimes these bodies pull gas from their companion stars and you see the gas swirling down toward the dark center. But you don't know where it's going and you don't learn anything about that central body except that it is dark and has a strong gravitational pull.

JK: Would you like to go into a wormhole?

KT: Well, I would like to know whether wormholes can even exist. If they can exist, yes, I would love to use a wormhole's tube, of space warpage to travel quickly to the far reaches of the universe. But I am certain that that is not going to happen in my lifetime. Building or manipulating wormholes, if they can exist at all, is as far beyond our ability today as space travel is beyond the ability of an amoeba.

JK: When you fantasize about time travel, do you see any possible time-warp entry points for human beings? Short of Michael Jackson freezing himself . . .

KT: There are certainly ways, if you have adequate technology, to travel very rapidly into the future. What we don't know is whether there are ways to travel into the past. I'm almost sure, from calculations that I and others have done with the laws of physics, that every device for backward time travel will self-destruct before you can use it. But I'm less sure than I was a week ago. Last weekend, I learned of a recent sophisticated and delicate analysis of a hypothetical time machine that was done at Montana State University by William Hiscock and Tsunefumi Tanaka. Hiscock and Tanaka found that for their version of a time machine the explosion would be less powerful than I had expected. Perhaps the machine would survive the explosion and could be used to go backward in time, but I doubt it. In any event, the technology for building such a time machine and trying it out is far far beyond our capabilities; we humans have no hope of doing so in the next several millennia.

Our struggle with the question of time travel is in itself a way to understand the nature of time. We don't have definitive answers, just strong indications. We physicists struggle not only with the longest times imaginable, tens of billions of years, but also with the shortest times imaginable. The self-destruction of a time machine occurs in a flash. It lasts something like 10^{-43} seconds, which is the shortest time interval that the laws of physics permit to exist. It's all quantifiable and it's all governed by these laws of physics that we can manipulate mathematically.

JK: Does the existence of other life in the universe seem inevitable?

KT: Not inevitable, but based on what we understand about biology, chemistry, astronomy, I'd be very surprised if the universe isn't teeming with it. I think the odds are reasonably good that, in my lifetime, humans will receive radio signals from distant star systems that prove the existence of other civilizations. A vigorous privately funded search for such radio waves is underway (public funding was recently wiped out by Congress), particularly at NASA's Ames Research Center in California. We can look out through a significant part of the galaxy and see television emanations produced by some distant civilization's version of Channel Five in L.A.

JK: Emanations that have traveled . . .

KT: That were produced, let's say, a hundred years ago on some planet around a star a hundred light years away. These civilizations do not need to consciously try to send signals to us. We just have to catch them in a phase in their evolution when they're using television transmissions and have not completely converted to optical fiber transmissions or other communication methods which wouldn't transmit signals out into space. We humans now have the technology to transmit and receive such signals across the vast reaches of interstellar space—and on that basis it seems very reasonable to look for transmissions from distant civilizations. The Search for Extraterrestrial Intelligence, or SETI, is one of the human race's most important endeavors, I believe.

JK: Why was public funding cut off? Was it considered too crackpot?

KT: It was considered crackpot by one or two key congressmen. There is no guarantee of seeing anything, but the chances are moderately good and the impact and the payoff, if successful, could be enormous. When the odds of success are moderate, as most of us think they are, it's simply foolish not to search. Fortunately, there are some wealthy philanthropists who are now funding the research.

JK: If SETI were to pinpoint transmissions from a distant planet that were sent as little as a hundred years ago, would we be at all capable of responding?

KT: We could certainly respond but it would take another two hundred years to receive their reply to our response. It would be a slow conversation.

JK: How would the response differ from the waves that we send out in our normal technological ways?

KT: Well, we may soon stop sending those waves out because we are converting from radio to optical communication. But if we beam a very large radio telescope in a particular direction, we can send a signal that will travel all the way across the galaxy and be seen at the other side in about a hundred thousand years. So communication is possible. Then there is the question of whether or not you want them to know we are here. There is the possibility that the beings on the other end are malevolent. Of course, we don't have control today over the fact that we have been emanating observable signals for the last fifty years. It's too late to hide ourselves.

JK: Can you hypothesize a malevolent signal?

KT: I can hypothesize that you would see something in the signal that would make you fear that, although the reaches of interstellar space are vast, they might come here to try to take us over, in the manner of a bad Hollywood movie. But luckily the odds of their having the technology to come here in less than a millennium are small.

JK: How do you keep your imagination in check, doing what you do?

KT: I enjoy the imaginary but, as in normal life, I try to make a clean distinction between reality and Walt Disney. I have a limited number of days on this earth and I would prefer to spend most of my time struggling to understand things that I'll be able to understand, at least in part.

Draft 24: Gap

Not under the clarity of the perfectly black square
  articulating pure erasure
where time or speech be emptied under the power
  of a power, the pwer precisely to quadrant the square
and indelibly to color it, acquiring points and promotions
  to higher pwr for the (dark) neatness and the (darker) lucidity
and the (darkest) completeness
  of the orderly achievement of erasure
(in our time),

but a thread
   twisted tensile yet sprung unweavable
a seam
   breaking inside existence
a vent
   that flanged

through dark, and between
  a wander, all awander
   fracture and hinge.

One asks for meaning
   and, faced with any bit of fleck along the crack,

is eager: is it

                         in that spot, can one care

for it, is it there?

Now is the now. No matter what. No readiness
for its ungrouted forms.
Meaning is in its lack and in its bet,
in trips that trigger rime.

Let these be called the (underwired) "chips
         of messianic time."

Then: Let coat collections for the cold.   And what
       sleeveless passages are, what tunnels
             iced by neon
trudged,
       steps echoing among statistics, and what
wanderers are,
           between hold and hole
                among the mille-letters' shifted marks.

      Who sits at the table when policy is set?

      The girder amid, within, among, above,
over, on   as if   I had been shot in the head that day
between   the rickety boards,   the middle of city nowhere, in
      construction, before visiting   the locked ward
sight-reading the interface   when the   potential antagonist
at the innermost court   did not strike.   Or so they said.
      Did not yet strike with full intent. Dd nt,   or strk
             a never (mean, a nerve), the   deep never
                  of the river   of parallels.

Inside the wish the thick-walled house
is useless.   No one can date blankness   Can one
from distant fragments turning   date it, the numb
        grayland gunmetal drypoint? count fissure as vision?
                            number nullus?

Shadows of the lost, can one want to touch the lock,
siphon the lack,
and push that door a little crack? or not?

Frenzied with mere pinholes of opening, letters
            flooded into the space like paint
                        and soaked the site
                            with unreadable stain. But nothing
heroic, nothing but
tacky shadow piles of
nous and nouns,
not irresistible, but chronic,
set among a grayish fog so deep one cannot compass where one is,
in the lost and found
of aphasia, which makes such wwords you never heard
and pain to hear,
such periphras "that thing you know, like uhh uhh uhh, what
you do that with"
or "with that"

that plunges us further into the irreconcilable.

Was there a choice?

            The specific densities
            of what happens or follows. As it
            does, it does.
            Unfolding gentle garlands of sound,

little phases that went nowhee

not a random place,

but a shadow face.

Unsayable, unsolvable—the whole is built on them.

The dispersion of letters across everything one touches
as if thousands of pages
were only prolegomena
to itself.

The question
                    just of "r."
                                        Dead, or dread,
it marks the distance
                    that the particulars scatter,

which if attended
                    would mire the watcher
                                in unparalleled mourning.

                    For "historical dead"
        is what   she wrote, but I   split down the selfsame question
                        had written "historical dread."

        Therefore there is no volta,
writing being mired forever, or whenever, in its own
inky letters,
        missing and present,
                        winding and unwinding,
segmenting indefinitely,
                    error, placement, gap, and spell.

Some now more voiceless side is even there,
      as maybe dropp a letter from your name
            but which one should you,

                                    ache l?

                October, a gap, then December 1994–February 1995

The citation from Benjamin, "Theses on the Philosophy of History" (as at the end of Draft 12: Diasporas) *and the girder from Reznikoff are clear enough. There are also unmarked words from Garrett Stewart, Hank Lazer, Colleen Lamos, Victoria Harrison, and Uwe Kraemer. I also use, with thanks, a 1994 review of* Drafts, *in which Caroline Bergvall gave, as my phrase, "historical dead" instead of "historical dread." Thereupon I include a number of intentional typographical errors in this work.*

The Continued Saga of an Amateur Photographer

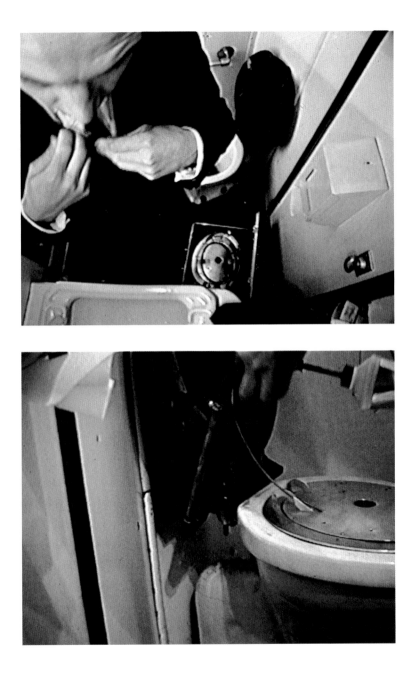

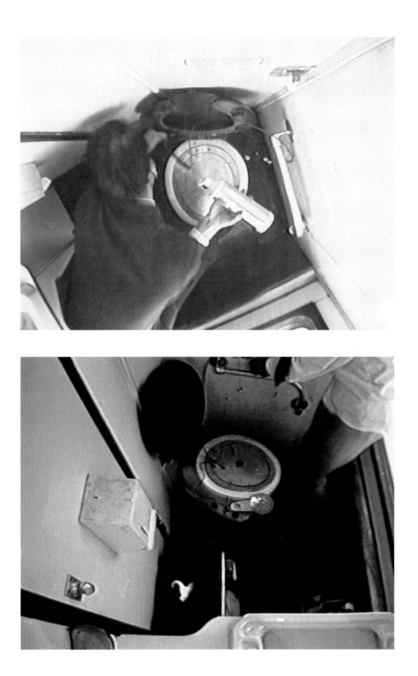

Above and left: Video stills taken from the film *The Continued Saga of an Amateur Photographer.*

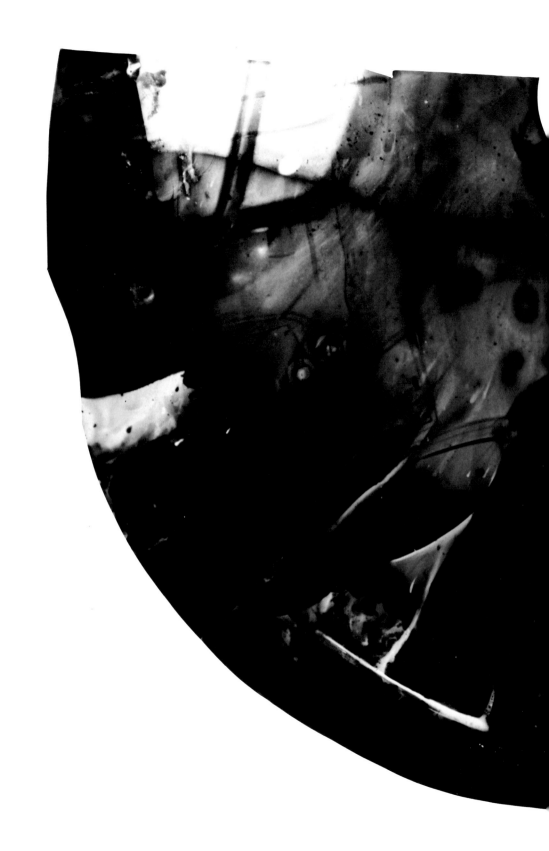

Exposure No. 6, British Rail Carriage No. 76805,
London to Brighton, 12:32 PM Train.

Exposure No. 10, British Rail Carriage No. 76578,
London to Brighton, 12:32 PM Train.

The Continued Saga of an Amateur Photographer, 1993

A toilet bowl on board a British Rail train traveling from London to Brighton was converted into a camera. First, a specially designed aluminum 'insert' was fitted into the recess of the toilet bowl. This device housed both lens and shutter device as well as a pneumatic seal which, when inflated with a bicycle pump, held the contraption firmly in place whilst also sealing out unwanted light. The operator then removed his trousers in order to 'load' the photographic paper, placing his arms down the trouser legs in the manner of a changing bag. After being 'exposed,' the toilet was flushed (taking care to avoid flushing while at a station), and developer was simultaneously injected into the toilet cistern pipe at the rear of the bowl. This operation was then repeated for the fixer after which the toilet was flushed again to wash the print of any residue chemicals. The print was then retrieved.

—Steven Pippin

Another Lost Empire

It. was. me. and. Jamieson.

Just us.

On this journey, this crazy high-speed journey through this strange land in this strange vehicle.

Just me and Sandy Jamieson.

But they were trying to disturb me, trying to wake me; the way they always did. They willnae let this sleeping dog lie. They always interfere. When the cunts start this shite it makes things get aw distorted and I have to try to go deeper.

DEEPER. Things get dis

                                        up – – – –
                                        coming
                                        start
                                        I
I lose control when they interfere – – – – and

—We're just going to take
your temperature, Roy. Have
you got the bedpan, Nurse
Norton? Number Twos now
Roy, time for Number Twos.
—Yes, he's looking brighter this morning, isn't he, Nurse Devine? You're brighter this
morning, Roy
lovey.

Aye right ye are, take your fuckin hand oot ma fuckin erse.

DEEPER

DEEPER –
– – – – – – – – – – Sandy Jamieson is my best friend down here. A former
professional sportsman and an experienced hunter of man-eating beasts,
I enlisted Jamieson's aid in a quest I have been engaged in for as long as
I can remember. However, as my memory is practically nonexistent, this
could have been a few days ago or since the beginning of time itself. I am,
for some reason, driven to eradicate the scavenger-predator bird known
as the Marabou Stork. I wish to drive this evil and ugly creature from the
African continent. In particular, I have this persistent vision of one large
blighter, a hideous and revolting specimen, which I know somehow must
perish by my own hand.

As with all other events, I have great difficulty in recalling how Sandy
Jamieson and I became friends. I do know that he was of great help to me
when I first came here, and that is enough. I do not wish to remember
where I was before. I am averse to my past; it is an unsavory blur which I
have no wish to attempt to pull into focus. Here and now, Africa and
Sandy, they are my present and my future.

I feel a cool breeze in my face and turn to face my companion. He's
in good spirits behind the wheel of our jeep.

—You've been at the wheel far too long, Sandy. I'll take over! I
volunteered.

—Wizard! Sandy replied, pulling over by the side of the track.

A large insect settled on my chest. I swatted the blighter. —Yuk! Those
insects, Sandy! How positively yucky!

—Absolutely, he laughed, clambering over into the back seat. —It'll be great to stretch these damn pins! He smiled, extending his long, tanned, muscular legs across the back seat.

I slid into the driver's seat and started up the jeep.

All Sandy and myself had in the world were this rotten old jeep, some limited supplies, and very little money. The majority of our possessions had recently been expropriated by a cunning but somewhat morally deficient native fellow, whom we'd rather foolishly hired as a guide.

For a while we had planned to engage the services of some young native boys, but the undernourished specimens we had encountered had proved to be unappetizing prospects... that is, manifestly unfit for the physical demands adventures with Sandy and I would inevitably place upon them. Eventually we secured the services of one shifty urchin who went by the name of Moses. We took this to be a sign of good luck. It proved anything but.

Moses hailed from one of the shantytowns that lined the banks of Lake Torto. While I have to admit that we were not in the position to be able to pay our manservants generously, our behavior toward Moses scarcely merited the response of this roguish boy: the blighter did a runner with the bulk of our money and supplies.

I find this attitude of "something for nothing" sadly prevalent amongst the non-white races, but I put the blame fairly and squarely on the shoulders of the white colonialists, who by assuming responsibility for

GOD THAT BLINDING   up – – –
BLOODY FUCKING   coming
SUN – – – – – – – – – – – – – – – – I'm

> —Roy, I'm shining this torch into your
> eyes. Pupil dilation seems more evident.
> Good. Good.

FUCK OFF

—Definitely more of a response that time, Roy. It's probably just a reflex, though. I'll try it again... no... nothing this time around.

Naw, cause I'm too quick for youse, you'll never find ays in here.

DEEPER

      DEEPER

            DEEPER – – – – – – – – – – – Sandy is masturbating in the back of the jeep and she is just laughing... eh ... what the fuck's gaun oan here... what's *she* daein here... it's just supposed tae be Sandy n me... I'm losing control and all I can hear is her laughter and I see her face in the mirror; her face warped and cartoonish as his semen shoots onto her blouse. Her face is like... is like I want to... I'm feeling jealous. Jealous of Jamieson. What I want is for her not to just sit there laughing, not to sit and encourage him; I want to scream, don't encourage him you fucking slut, but I have to concentrate on the road because I've never driven before....

I can't keep my eyes off Sandy Jamieson. There is a sick tribe of demons lurking behind his generous if gormless facade. I am moved to shout, —You're a metaphor, Jamieson. You don't exist outside of me. I can't be angry with nothing, you're just a manifestation of my guilt. You're a projection.

This is ridiculous. Sandy's my friend. My guide. The best friend I've ever had but

But Jamieson now has his penis in her mouth. Its head bubbles her cheek outward from the inside. It looks horrible, that swelling, that distortion of her face. Sandy's face, though, is even worse; it reddens and inflates, providing a contrast to his dark, shaven head and the whites around his dark green eyes. —I'm real enough, he gasps, —this rod is in your girlfriend's head.

In my mirror, while at the same time trying to keep my eyes on the dusty, winding track that they ridiculously refer to as a road, I see a blade come tearing out of her face. Panic sets in as I realize that the vehicle I'm traveling in is a structure now indivisible from my own body and we're dipping and flipping over, rising upward in a shuddering rush into a buzzing wall of light. I'm gulping frenziedly at air which is so thick and heavy it feels like water in my lungs. I hear the shrieks of a large predatory bird soaring past me; so close to my head I can smell the diseased remnants of carrion from it. I regain some sense of control over the vehicle only to find that she's gone and Jamieson is sitting in the front passenger seat with me.

—It was getting a tad crowded back there, he smiles, gesturing behind us to a trio of Japanese men in business suits who are occupying the back seat. They are excitedly snapping with cameras and speaking in a language which I can't make out but which doesn't seem to be Japanese.

This is totally fucked.

Is Sandy the best guide in all of this?

DEEPER

        DEEPER

                DEEPER

Yes.

I'm starting to feel happier. The deeper I get, the further away from them I get, the happier I feel. Sandy Jamieson's expression has changed. He is reassuming the persona of a loyal friend and guide, rather than that of a sneering adversary. This means I'm back to where they can't get to me: deep in the realms of my own consciousness.

But they keep trying; even from in here I can feel them. Trying to stick another tube up my arse or something similar, something which constitutes a breach of my personal no no can't have this... change the subject, keep control.

Control.

Sandy

DEEPER

        DEEPER

                DEEPER – – – – – – – – – – – – – – Holy Cow! Sandy exclaimed as an unwanted Marabou Stork flew past the passenger window. I knew that it was our bird, but pursuit was difficult, as I had little control over this vehicle. The bird was impossible to follow in flight, but later on we would endeavor to locate its nest on the ground and destroy the beast. As things stood, however, we were coming down slowly, with a strange hydraulic hiss, toward the surface of this tropical, forested terrain.

—I've absolutely no control here, Sandy, I defeatedly observed, pulling at levers and pushing at buttons, but to little avail. I threw my hands up in exasperation. I wanted to stay up here. It seemed important not to land.

—Any biscuits left, Roy? Sandy asked eagerly.

I looked at the packet on the dashboard. There were only three left which meant that the greedy blighter had scoffed most of them!

—Gosh Sandy, you're a Hungry Horace today, I remarked.

Sandy gave out a high, clear laugh. —Nerves, I suppose. I don't particularly want to land, but at least this place might have some proper tuck.

—I hope so! I said.

The craft descended implacably, coming down over what at first seemed to be a small settlement, but which appeared to be expanding continually beyond our line of vision until we saw it as a giant metropolis. We were hovering down into this old stone colonial building which had no roof, only the jagged remnants of glass around the periphery showing where one had been.

I thought that our craft would never squeeze through the gap and braced myself for collision. However, its dimension seemed to alter to fit the shape it had to go through, and we touched down in a rather splendid hall with some interesting Gothic stonework. This was obviously some sort of public building, its grandeur hinting at more affluent times and its poor state of maintenance indicative of a more sordid and less civic present.

—Do you think we're allowed here, Sandy asked shakily.

—I don't see why not. We're explorers, aren't we, I told him.

As we got out of our car (for this was what the vehicle now seemed to be, a simple family saloon car) we noted the presence of many people, wandering around aimlessly, and taking little notice of us. Some broken glass crunched under my feet. I started to feel more than a wee bitty paranoid, thinking that the natives would perhaps blame us for breaking the roof. While we were innocent, circumstantial evidence could certainly be weighted against us by an unscrupulous and malevolent set of officials in a corrupt regime, which to a greater or lesser extent meant any regime. I had absolutely no intention of getting back into that vehicle, nor, evidently, had Sandy; engaged as he was in the removal of his backpack which contained half our supplies. I followed his lead and swung my own pack over my shoulders.

—Strange little performance this, I noted, turning to Jamieson, who was surveying the scene with increasing distaste. Two white men walked straight past us, completely ignoring us. I was just starting to entertain the possibility that we were invisible when Sandy roared, —This is preposterous! I am a seasoned explorer and a professional footballer! I demand to be treated in a sporting manner!

—It's okay, Sandy, I smiled, placing a comforting hand on my friend's shoulder.

This outburst was certainly effective in registering our presence, but only at the expense of generating hostility from some of the citizens present. In particular, one band of youthful roughs was sizing us up.

Gosh and golly.

Damn and fucking blast.

—Sandy's the *enfant terrible* of British soccer,
I limply endeavored to explain.   up – – – Okay Roy?
Then I felt something – – – – – – – – – – – – – coming

AH FEEL SOMETHING AH FEEL IT BUT YOUSE CUNTS CAN FUCK OFF AND DIE CAUSE YOUSE'LL NO GIT AYS IN HERE YA CUNTS DEEPER
       DEEPER
             DEEPER – – – – —Let's scarper, Sandy, I nodded, noting that the mood of the mob had turned sour and – – – coming up – – – oh fuck I've lost control again THESE CUNTS' FAULT, LEAVE AYS ALANE and now I feel the stabbing beak in my arm, it can only be the Marabou Stork but it's my injection, it's the chemicals, not ones that dull and chill my brain, not ones that make me forget, because with these ones I remember.

Oh my God, what dae ah fuckin well remember. . .

Lexo said that it was important that we didnae lose our bottle. Nae cunt was tae shite oot; eftir aw, the fuckin hoor asked fir it. She'd've goat it fae some cunts anywey the wey she fuckin well carried oan and the fuckin fuss she made. Aye, she goat slapped aroond a bit, but we wir fuckin vindicated, British justice n that. She wis jist in the wrong place at the wrong time n anywey it wis aw Lexo's fault. . .

. . . change the subject. . . I don't want this. I want to keep hunting the Stork. The Stork's the personification of all this badness. If I kill the Stork I'll kill the badness in me. Then I'll be ready to come out of here, to wake up, to take my place in society and all that shite. Ha. They'll get a fuckin shock, when they see this near-corpse, this package of wasting flesh and bone just rise and say: —Awright chavvy! How's tricks?

Awright son!

AW FUCK! *THEY'RE* HERE. ALWAYS FUCKIN HERE. ALWAYS ASSUMING I WANT THEIR FUCKIN PRESENCE. DAE THEY NO HAVE FUCKING VISITING HOURS HERE?

My father. Nice to see you, Dad. Please continue, while I doze.

—How ye daein? Eh? Well, that's us in another final. Disnae seem two whole years since the, eh, accident, but enough ay that. Another final! One-nil. Darren Jackson. Ah didnae go masel mind. Tony wis thair. Ah wis gaunny go, bit ah nivir goat a ticket. Saw it oan the telly. Like ah sais, one-nil. Darren Jackson, Barry goal n aw. Tony made up a tape ay the commentary, like ah sais, a tape eh made up. Eh Vet?

—Aye.

—Ye goat the tape then?

—What?

—The tape, Vet. Ah'm askin ye, ye goat the tape?

—Tape . . .

—Whit's wrong, Vet?

—Thir's a Jap ower thair, John.

—It's jist a nurse, Vet, jist a nurse. Probably no even a Jap. Probably a Chinky or somethin. Eh son? Jist a nurse ah'm sayin, son. Eh Roy? Eh that's right son?

FUCK OFF AND DIE YOU DAFT AULD CUNT

—A nurse . . .

—Aye, the wee Chinky nurse. Nice lassie. Eh son? Lookin better the day though, son. Mair color. Like ah sais, eh Vet, like ah sais, Roy's goat mair color aboot um.

—They nivir git it. Every other perr bugger gits it, but they nivir git it.

—Eh?

—AIDS. Ye nivir see Japs wi AIDS. Here wuv goat it. In America thuv goat it. In India thuv goat it. In Africa thuv goat it. Oor Bernard might huv it. No thaim, though. They nivir git it.

—What the fuck ye oan aboot? Chinky nurse . . . nice wee lassie . . .

—Ken how? Ken how they nivir git it?

—Vet, this husnae goat nowt tae dae wi . . .

—Cause they inventit it! They inventit the disease! So as they could take over the world!

—You fuckin stupit or somethin?! Talkin like that in front ay Roy! Ye dinnae ken what the laddie kin hear, how it affects um! Like ah sais, ye fuckin stupit? Ah'm askin ye! Ye fuckin stupit?

MUMMY DADDY, NICE TO SEE YOU IS IT FUCK DON'T WANT TO SURFACE DON'T WANT TO GET CLOSER TO YOUR UGLY WORLD GOT TO GO DEEPER, DEEPER DOWN, GOT TO HUNT THE STORK, TO GET CONTROL

DEEPER
      DEEPER
            DEEPER – – – – – – – – – – – – – – –
– –Jamieson.

We've somehow given the baying mob the slip and find ourselves on the edge of a run-down shantytown. A huge, festering garbage dump lies alongside a now poisonous lake. Malnourished children play in its squalor. Some of them come over to Sandy and myself, begging without really expecting any results. One little boy, a wild-looking creature with a face as brown as dark chocolate, stares intently at us, never averting his gaze. He is wearing nothing but old, dirty blue shorts and a pair of worn shoes without any socks.

—I say, Roy, what an extraordinary-looking creature, Sandy smiled.

—Yes, a funny little thing, I said.

The little boy gave a loud, long laugh and suddenly poured out quite an extended speech. I couldn't understand a bloody word of it.

—Bantu, I suppose, Sandy said sadly. —Sounds all very splendid and lovely, but I can't make head nor tail of it!

We gave them some coins and Sandy produced a small bag of sweets. —If we only had a ball, I could do a bit of coaching, get a scratch game up, he said wistfully.

I looked up at the blinding sun. It had been relentless all day, but soon it would retreat behind the green hills which rose up over the Emerald Forest. This was a beautiful spot. This... my thoughts were distracted by some shouts and the sound of the rattling of tin against the compressed clay track. Jamieson was expertly shielding a Coca Cola can from the rangy limbs of a group of the local Bantu children. —There you go, you little blighters... it's all about possession, he told them.

He was forever the sport.

While Sandy's interest in sports coaching and the development of youth was touching, we had more pressing matters to consider. Our vehicle had been left behind in the civic hall, neither of us caring to travel in anything quite so unreliable. —We need transport, Sandy, I told him, —our Stork must be nesting around here somewhere.

Sandy signaled for the kids to disperse. One tyke, our funny little creature, glared at me in a sulky way. I hated to be the spoilsport, but there was business to take care of.

Sandy crisply and clinically volleyed the can into the rubbish-infested lake, then looked at me and shook his head sadly. —This is not going to be quite as straightforward as you think, Roy. The Storks are dangerous and formidable opponents. We're alone and isolated in hostile terrain, without any supplies or equipment, he explained. Then he looked at me with a penetrating stare, —Why is slaying that large

Marabou so important to you?

Damn and fucking blast.

This made me stop to consider my motives. Oh yes, I could have gone on about the spirit of the hunt. I could have produced a welter of damning evidence of the carnage that these despicable beasts can perpetrate on other wildlife and game; on how they can upset the entire ecology of a region, how they can spread pestilence and disease through the local villages. Certainly, such reasoning would have struck a chord with both Sandy's sense of adventure and his humanitarian principles.

The problem is it wouldn't have been true. Moreover, Sandy would have known that I was lying.

I cleared my throat, and turned away from the blinding sun. Feeling a shortness of breath, I felt the words about to evaporate in my throat as I prepared to speak them. I always seem to feel something sticking in my throat. I cough, miraculously finding strength, and carry on. —I can't really explain, Sandy, not to my own satisfaction, so certainly not to anyone else's. I just know that I've met that Stork before, in a previous life perhaps, and I know that it's evil. I know that it's important for me to destroy it.

Sandy stood looking at me for a few seconds, his countenance paralyzed with doubt and fear.

—Trust me on this one, mate? I said softly.

His face ignited in a beautiful, expansive smile, and he gave me a powerful hug which I reciprocated. We broke off and gave each other the high-five. —Let's do the blighter! Sandy smiled, a steely glint of determination entering his eye.

Another two small black children from the football game aproached us. Their clothes were in tatters. —Homosexual? One young boy asked. —I suck you off for rand.

Sandy looked down at the crusty-lipped urchin. —Things may be bad, little one, but selling your body to the white man is not the answer. He ruffled the child's hair and the boy departed, skipping across the path back down toward the settlement.

We moved on by foot, carrying our backpacks and heading out of the village toward the other side of the lake. The wind had changed direction and the smell from the rubbish was overpowering in the hazy heat. Ugly bugs of varied sizes swarmed around us, forcing us to beat a hasty retreat along the path. We ran until we couldn't go any further, although I must confess that was the royal "we," for Sandy, as a professional sportsman, had quite an edge on me in fitness and stamina, and could probably have stuck it out a bit longer.

We set up camp with our provisions, enjoying a feast in a shady glade by the more picturesque side of the lake. We opened our packs to examine their contents.

—Mmmm! Pork pie; homemade of course, said Sandy.

—And what's this . . . golly, it's a cheese! How enormous. Smell it, Sandy, it's enough to make you want to start eating straight away!

—Gosh, I can't wait to get my mouth around that, Sandy smiled.

—And that homemade bread! Can't we start?

—No, there are new-laid boiled eggs to begin with, I laughed.

—Gosh, all we're missing is some homemade apple pie and ice cream, Sandy smiled, as we tucked in to our feast. Then, suddenly inspired, he turned to me and said, —I've got it, Roy! What we need is sponsorship! Somebody to fund this Stork hunt. I know a chap who'll sort us out with provisions. He runs the Jambola Safari Park, access to which is a few miles' trek on the west side of the lake.

I knew instantly who Sandy was talking about. —Dawson. Mr. Lochart Dawson.

—You know him?

I shrugged noncommittally. —I know *of* him. Then again, most people know of Lochart Dawson. He sees to that.

—Yes, he has a flair for self-publicity, does our Lochart, Sandy said, his tone implying an affectionate familiarity. I then recalled that Sandy mentioned that he'd previously been in the employ of Dawson.

Sandy was correct about the self-publicity; you just couldn't keep Dawson out of the news. He was currently planning on expanding his park by taking over an adjacent leisure reserve. Whether in the long term Dawson actually envisaged any animals in what he described as the "superpark" was more open to conjecture. He had made his money in the development of property, and there were more profitable uses for land in this region than a safari park. Nonetheless, Dawson could be useful.

—We'd have a smashing time at old Dawson's, I said eagerly.

—I'll bet he's got enough food to feed an army! Sandy agreed. Suddenly we were interrupted by a chorus of frenetic squawking. We looked back, and I saw them. Although one or two social group-ings could be evidenced, they were largely standing in isolation from each other, in the rubbish by the lakeside. Some squatted on their breasts, others paced slowly at a short distance. One large devil; it must have had a wing span of around eighty and weighed about nine kilos, turned its back to the sun and spread its wings, exposing those spare filamentous black feathers.

The beast's throat patch was reddish; it had scabs of warty dried blood on the base of its large, conical bill; its legs were stained white with dried excrement. It was the large, bulky scavenger-predator known as the Marabou Stork. More importantly, it was our one.

—Look Sandy, once again I felt my words dry in my throat, as I pointed across the lake to the mountain of rubbish and the large bird.

The sheer evil power of the creature emanating from its deathly eyes shook us to the marrow.

—Come ahead then, ya fuckin wide-os! It squawked.

I felt sick and faint.

Sandy looked pretty fazed.

—Look Roy, we need more hardware to take on that bastard. Its bill must be razor-sharp, containing the venom and poison of rotting carcasses: one scratch could be fatal. Let's see Dawson. His resort was once plagued by these beasts, but he found a way to sort them out.

THESE BEASTS ARE KILLERS. THEY ARE INTERESTED ONLY IN MAYHEM. THEY CARE NOTHING FOR THE GAME...

up – – –

back

Eh?   coming

Aw fuck – – – – I'm

—We're away now, son.
Yir Ma n me. Like ah sais
that's us away now.
CHEERIO SON! CHEERIO ROY!
—Cheerio Roy! Cheerio darlin.

—Like yir Ma sais, that's us sayin cheerio. See ye the morn though son. Ah'll be in the morn. CHEERIO ROY!

Aye, aye, aye. He's always so fuckin loud. Ah'm no fuckin deef, ya cunt! Sometimes ah just feel it would be so much fuckin easier tae just open my eyes and scream: FUCK OFF!

—The min-it choo walked in the joint dih-dih, I could see you were a man of dis-tinc-tyin, a real big spender...

What the fuck is this? Ma. She's finally fuckin blown it.

—... good loo-kin, so ree-fined...

—What ur ye daein Vet? Whit the fuck ye playin at?

—Bit mind they sais John, mind they sais that ah could sing tae um. The doaktirs said. Ken, wi the music hittin a different part ay the brain. That's how wi bring in the tapes, John.

Ah just thoat this wid mean mair tae the laddie, like say a live performance. Mind eh eywis liked ays singing Big Spender whin eh wis a bairn?

　　—Aye, well music n singin, that's different like. Different sort ay things. That's jist singin you're daein. Ye couldnae really call it music, Vet. Like ah sais, ye couldnae really call it music.

　　—Bit ah could git Tony tae play the guitar. Make up a tape ay me singin Big Spender, fir the laddie's cassette player, John. Ah could dae that, John.

　　OH FUCKIN HELL, GOD PRESERVE US...

　　I could tell that my Ma was upset, and they had another blazing argument. I was relieved when they departed. So fuckin relieved. Even now they embarrass me. Even in here. I've nothing to say to them; I don't think anything of them. I never really had, besides I was anxious to get back to Sandy and our pursuit of the Stork. I hear a different voice now though, a sort of fluffy feminine voice, the voice of Nurse Patricia Devine. —That's the visitors away now, Roy.

　　Her voice is soft, mildly arousing. Maybe I'll get a bit of love interest into my little fantasy, a bit a shagging into things no no no there will be no shagging because that's what caused aw this fuckin soapy bubble in the first place and I'm being turned over in my decaying organic vehicle, and I can feel the touch of Patricia Devine.

　　Can I feel her touch, or do I just think I can? Did I really hear my parents or was it all my imagination? I know not and care less. All I have is the data I get. I don't care whether it's produced by my senses or my memory or my imagination. Where it comes from is less important than the fact that it *is*. The only reality is the images and texts.

　　—There's nothing of you, she says to me cheerfully. I can feel the frost in the air. The staff nurse has given Patricia Devine a dirty look for making a negative comment in front of the veg. Me who used to weigh thirteen and a half stone, too. At one time I was heading for Fat Hell (Fathell, Midlothian, population 8,619) with a fat wife, fat kids, and a fat dog. A place where the only thing thin is the paycheck.

　　Now I can hear that "Staff" has departed leaving me with the simply Devine Patricia. Patricia is possibly an old hound, but I like to think of her as young and lovely. The concept adds quality to my life. Not a lot of things do at the moment. Only I add the quality. As much or as little as I want. If only they'd just fuckin leave ays tae get on with it. I don't need their quality, their world, that fucked-up place which made me the fucked-up mess I was. Down here in the comforts of my vegetative state, inside my secret world I can fuck who I want, kill who I please, no no no nane ay that no no no I can do the things I wanted to do, the things I tried to do, up there in the real world. No comeback. Anyway, *this* world's real enough to me and I'll stay down here out of the way, where they can't get to me, at least until I work it all out.

It hasn't been so easy recently. Characters and events have been intruding into my mind, psychic gatecrashers breaking in on my private party. Imposing themselves. Like Jamieson, and now this Lochart Dawson. Somehow, though, this has given me a sense of purpose. I know why I'm in here. I'm here to slay the Stork. Why I have to do this I do not know. I know that I need help, however, and I know that Jamieson and Dawson are my only potential allies in this quest.

This is what I have instead of a life.

You Dropped Something

So what if it's brackish my love
today's junk mail is full of arms for you
the erotic weavings of slumlord
hermits and piss-elegant diatribes:
no more waving for you
at least for the time being
which is anybody's stable

The lost nights thatched with regrets
shingled with antinomian heresy and hedged
about with ifs ands and buts
are nobody's dream cycle to you
the arena of matches and pups

and further slide
into romantic chaos
Say they're not keeping track anymore
that the wounded demoiselle is hopping
mad and more coal barges
have arrived on the harbor's
slippery surface

Say then that they're not well again
Jumping through hoops to train
myself to attract attention was always
sometimes my endeavor to attract
smart eyes

You that go out and go in
through memory's many castles
are you single or just alone this evening
castrati belch forth some
air thought to be unfit
for today's goads and geodes

She'll be coming round the house
and faster too; some press goodies
overlooked in the mad rush to prepubescent freedom
whose minds got mismatched

Throw many more daggers at the stone
It's ancient after all
how many comic strips do you invoke
what tarheels
in fashionable disarray
more strokes this morning

You come to the end of a row
you could switch over or begin a new one
at the wrong end and work back to the previous beginning
Do we really want to see it turn out all right
Are the guns trained on her
quarterdeck what about the ketch

And do you really go in

It's a passably elegant solution
for what was only land office before
ancient miles of wind picking
the harrow clean
All standing around
just to welcome you

you and your pie-eyed souvenir chest
and the bride you brought from back east
nailed to the sun

The Penitent

What are these apples doing here?
I thought I told you never to bring them inside.

And that wedding cake—what does it think it is?
Promises? Was it for this I sublet the apartment,

consecrated myself to a life of prudery
and banal satisfaction? I could have sold my life

story to a famous writer. But by then
it would have been over. Too much to write about isn't a good thing.

He recognized me! The famous man
knew my name! He held my hand

a second. I'd do that for someone.
The library is too fast tonight,

there's some spoilage in the lagoon, but everyone
is looking forward to your coming of age,

to the diamond stickpin and the hat.
Yet others carp,

seek annoyance, complain of the shadow,
as though 'twere always dusky night,

but your face looks good in the bathroom mirror.
I like your air freshener, your after-shave—

Say, what is it you do to look and smell so good?
Methinks some of it might come off on me

in the forest, with the cool sky
ambient with rubbings.

THE COLLYER BROTHERS

The story of the Collyer Brothers, Langley and his blind brother, Homer, is one in which the lives of objects come to rule the lives of people; where any attempt to comprehend, distinguish, or manage possessions is outstripped by their proliferation beyond control.

In 1909, Langley and Homer Collyer renounced the wealth and society they had grown up with to share a hermit-like existence in their decaying, three-story brownstone at Fifth Avenue and 128th Street. When, almost forty years later, New York City police received a mysterious telephone call alerting them to a possible death at the Collyer residence, they were completely unprepared for what they found. The rooms of the house they entered were filled to the ceiling with piles of neatly wrapped newspapers, cardboard boxes, books, and miscellaneous objects, and were traversable only through various hidden maze-like tunnels that had been carved through the debris. Police found Homer, 65, in a chair in an upstairs room, dead of a heart attack. When no trace could be found of Langley Collyer, 61, they left the building.

Three days after first entering the house, police began searching the building for Langley Collyer, who had not surfaced elsewhere, but could not find him. The Public Administrator's Office then took charge of the house, removing 120 tons of miscellaneous objects—including fourteen grand pianos, a pipe organ, an old generator, and the chassis of a Model-T Ford. Much of the treasure, acquired by both salvage and purchase and hoarded by the Collyers, wound up on the auction block.

On April 8, 1947, eighteen days after the original search, Langley's body was found ten feet from the chair in which Homer had died, in a tunnel beneath four feet of accumulated rubbish. Police concluded that Langley had fallen victim to one of the numerous booby traps he had scattered throughout the junk-cluttered building. The fact that his legs had already been gnawed by rats led detectives to believe that Langley had, in fact, died before Homer.

In the following years a mordant simile circulated in New York City: anyone guilty of clutter was accused of "living like the Collyer Brothers."

3/22/47
G. William
Collyer, of
Rutherford, N.J.,
an uncle, and his
son, G. Douglas
Collyer, peer
into the home
of the recluse
Collyer brothers,
Homer and Langley.

3/24/47 A crowd watches the debris-cluttered Collyer mansion (building nearest camera) on upper Fifth Avenue. Thousands gathered daily to watch police search the house.

3/25/47 A New York City policeman climbs over debris to enter the junk-filled library in the Collyer house, during search

3/25/47 Lt. Ed Stanley (left) and Deputy Inspector Tom Boylan of the New York City Police point to "booby trap" box set to topple all the rubbish if disturbed.

3/24/47   Patrolman George McLaughlin of the New York City Police
holds up a decaying auto steering wheel found in the Collyer mansion.

3/24/47 Chief Inspector John O'Connor of the New York City Building and Housing Department jams his way through a tunnel which ran up a staircase from the first floor.

4/8/47 An unidentified detective looks at the body of Langley Collyer after a layer of four feet of rubbish has been cleared away.

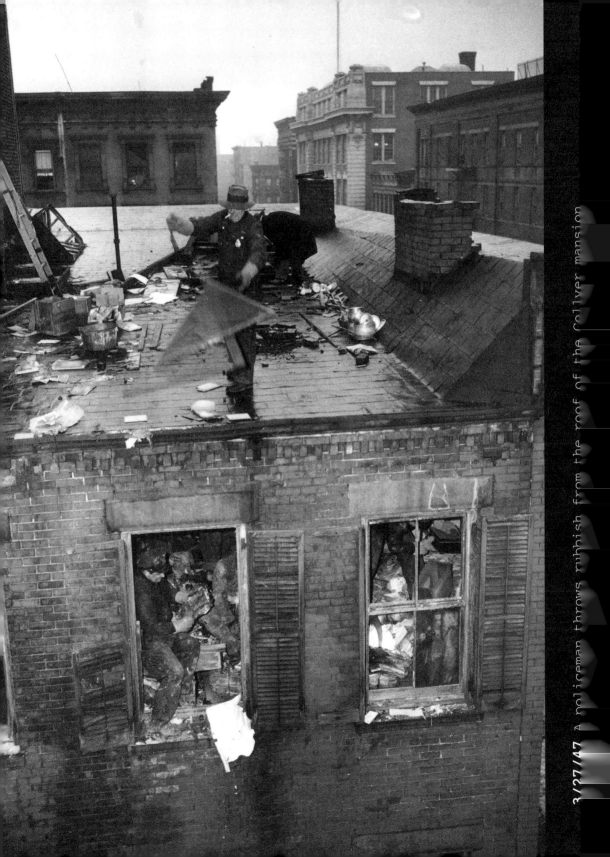

Painted

She had got used to addressing the servants in her own language.

.

Raucous laughter
opaque as the Chinese magazine I bought today
for the pictures of naked women. On the bar
branches of cherry blossoms.

.

Tattoo of heels.

.

Stepin Fetchit in whiskers.

.

A labor dispute among the reindeer.

.

Hunting the celebrity trophy   Bambi
Rudolph   Dumbo.

.

Society is all but rude
To this delicious solitude.

.

All you can eat.

.

In the midst of great happiness
listen to the voice inside you crying
'desist, desist.'

.

Swan-luminous night.

.

Golden
as a crust of bread.

.

The smell of grapes.
Lost
amid vine-clad.

.

A careful man
dips his brush   the tip
a cone of black.

.

Like a swan's neck.

.

She thought that motherhood was a fine thing she thought
that children should be seen and not heard she
thought that children should have their
heads shaved, their
own world, a bathtub, a
doubtful plaything. She
paid attention to her friends' children she thought it
was fine for a child to bite the dog she was an
unripe fig, a
flower, an
unbroken seed.

.

A gesture, as if
suddenly naked, had discovered
her nakedness   the hand
between them shielding her face.

.

Floats into his arms as if the air
were liquid.

.

Body hunger
found and lost
repeats and repeats
and finally comforted. Look,
the storm
is what saves, the bed
a sort of cradle.

.

Riding my bike through the dogwoods   busts
of poets in "blind rapture,"
girls in white, pulled by large
dogs, fragile
as a bough of blossoms.

.

At the bandshell
cameras
and small girls in leotards.
Small comforts,
dreams of grace.

.

Dip the brush lightly,
just the tip,
come away pink
and touch the paper.

.

Embracing sleep itself.
A place with songbirds.

Bright Winter

We believe it to be a case of life and death. It is death to remain connected with those bodies that speak lightly of, or oppose, the coming of the Lord. It is life to come out from all human tradition, and stand upon the Word of God . . . We therefore now say to all who are in any way entangled in the yoke of bondage, "Come out from among them, and be ye separate, saith the Lord."

Joshua V. Himes, in the imminent-advent newspaper,
The Midnight Cry, *August 29, 1844*

Broadhill,
January 12th

John Ephraim,

If I chose to I could find you and bring you home. I am known in the several towns where you may be lodged, even as far as Grasstown where the mayor once welcomed my money. Favors are owed to me up and down this county. I could employ men to go around the towns and knock on the doors and demand that the landladies array their boarders on the steps. This would flush you out eventually, no matter how you covered your ears and ignored the noise. But why should your foolishness disrupt my day's work? Duty and self-regard forbid me to go snuffing at your footprints. I shall simply write, and make several copies and distribute them around to those you may have dealings with. In this way you may receive a letter and be assured of my feelings in this matter, that is to say, irked, and faintly amused.

The horse you rode I will consider leased by the day. I will determine the schedule of repayment when you have come home.

Your mother is cheerful but weak, and stays abed. She does not know you've gone. I have said you are traveling with Daniel Kimball to hear the concerts at Braxton. A lie.

your Father

Broadhill,
January 16th

John Ephraim,

Perhaps shame has made you shy. But let me say that if you will see your error and come back, we will forget this episode. It will never color our relations in the future. And your mother need never know.

your Father

January 19th

John Ephraim,

I have had no response from you this week. Twice I sent letters to the Congregation men of Braxton, Lewiston, Rocky Ford, Carlisle, and Grasstown. I have of course bound them to discretion, as reputations are not easily repaired in this county. One letter went along in the pocket of James Spencer, who was traveling to Lewiston. His Marie asks after you, he tells me. I was silent, unwilling to lie—a rude man and a bad neighbor. For this I thank you. The other letters I took myself. I gave them to these church men because who knows where your fellows may gather to worship—I know only that some of them have been expelled from their congregations, and that these ministers may be able to name them. So this is what you want. To leave the world of warm society and sensible character. To shame your family into lies.

Not a man has seen you in any town. I made discreet inquiry, saying my son had passed through recently and asking, had he stopped in to pass the time? No? A heedless young man, too thoughtful, too studious, and thus rude. In this way I dressed your disrespect in the clothes of a common flaw. Again and again, I gave a chuckle that hurt my throat.

But no one had seen you. Once I asked myself if you might be hurt, struck down by robbers on a road. But no. We argued, and you have taken yourself off on your own legs for your own fool's vision. Moreover on my travels a corroborating rumor came to my attention. This was in the hatter's shop in Rocky Ford. The hatter had heard of a gathering, an encampment across the river. People of all kinds were wading the ford with their children, he said, even carrying their babies still in skirts. They've come to play at some absurd game, he said, they're bewitched by preachers with loud voices who rattle chains. And why they chose us, a sensible township, I don't know. Perhaps because they could get space near the river, and so carry water a shorter distance.

I said, Some people will let their fields to any rabble with cash.

You may be among these feverish pilgrims wetting their toes at the ford. Perhaps you wonder if I was tempted to cross and look for you. I was not. My equilibrium is not such that a gadding child can disturb it, and I had business at the bank. My goodbye to the hatter was comfortable. I've known him for years.

Your silence perplexes me, John Ephraim.

your Father

January 24th

John Ephraim,

My hand begins to tire from copy..ng letters. Colleagues at the bank have noticed it shake a bit when I sign my name. They wonder, too, why I send these letters out to Lewiston, Rocky Ford, Carlisle, Grasstown. They may believe I correspond with creditors. Or, perhaps, a woman. They may be saying Josiah Cole has turned from his wife in her illness.

But now I need not copy. I need send only to the minister Gearhart at Rocky Ford, who will find a suitable messenger. I am sure you are there.

For the story of the great blue tent erected at the crook of the river has appeared in the newspapers amid great joking. It's said that wild-eyed unmarried women make up the majority of the congregation, and are given to shouting prayers until they lose strength and must be carried out. Then there are drinkers, crawling babies, servants, and shaking old men who sing. A respectable community, my son! I see that there are many who share your brooding reading of Revelations, many others who have sat in their attics over the last year eschewing decent work and company, totting up numbers from the Bible as though God would speak to us in some heathenish code. There is even a report that your fellows have ordered a hundred bolts of white cloth, that they may sew robes to wear when they ascend. This sewing at least might some-day get you respectable employment. We've had tailors in the family before this, and you've already shown you don't mind spending time on your knees. Do you sleep on the ground with strangers, John Ephraim? Pardon my interest. I understand that they are brothers to you, and will live with you when God has annihilated the rest of us in a storm of fire. Well that you should learn their names, I suppose.

I scarcely dare hope that you have sent a letter crossing this, explaining.

your Father

January 25th

John Ephraim,

Let me amend the common saying and tell you that there's no great tomfoolery without some small gain. I had stopped over for supper with Mr. Partle, the new lawyer, and his wife. There was a good roast of pork and a glass of sherry and pleasant talk. The Partle boy is down at college and will begin to learn law in the autumn. Peculiar how many people seem to plan on autumn actually arriving.

Partle told me of a story he'd heard, that a woman out in Missouri had suckled an elk and raised it as her child. At least, several people had told him it was true. I opined that we were living in a climate of odd gullibility. Of course I did not elaborate. But see how my point was made for me! As I sat with Partle, there was a knock at the door, and on the stoop was a visitor looking for me. I recognized Will Whiting, our hired man years ago when you were a boy. Do you remember him? The one with a face like a shrew, who could not converse with your mother because he was always hiding his teeth.

Will, I said, it's quite a surprise. I thought you were in Indiana with the railroad.

I was, he said, but I've come back with a bad conscience. He took a little parcel from inside his coat. I opened it. Seven dollars in coin.

He said, When I worked for you I stole seven dollars. Now I'm here to settle my accounts. The Lord is coming, he said, and I want to go to meet him free and clear.

And out he goes! Partle and I had a little laugh over him. To think of old Will Whiting taking his soul so seriously. So the advent-near may have seduced my son, but it has at least given me seven dollars. Partle thought he'd write to all his old hired men anonymously and give them a little shove.

your Father

January 27th

John Ephraim,

Naturally I have had to tell your mother. You may not have considered when you left that she would long for you. Last night she listened to my excuse, and lifted her hand off the blanket.

Enough, now, Josiah, she said. Did he become ill traveling? What is there to tell?

I brought her the newspaper and held the lamp to it. She read slowly.

She said, It's the same as he has been saying these ten months. That God will come to us in the springtime.

They seem very confident, I told her.

So there is no use in planting seeds this year? she asked. Nor in other work?

I told her, No. Nor in repairing the barn or training the foals.

No use to send for a French bonnet?

No use to convert the native. No use to marry.

To marry was ever useless, she said. Oh, your mother smiling.

Then she said, He told us we were in danger. The foolish virgins who keep no oil in their lamps will be shut out from the wedding feast. Ah. This was the danger. Our young man gone.

This is beyond a jest. It is time for you to clear your head and come home.

your Father

February 2nd

John Ephraim,

No answer from you so I will not write.

your Father

February 3rd

John Ephraim,

Gearhart writes that he gives my letters to an old man who claims to belong to your blue congregation. He cannot take them himself, as he is too busy with his own alarmed and talkative flock. But he is not sure this fellow, a troubled drinker of spirits, and full of self-praise, tells him the truth. So I do not know if you read my lines and ignore them, or never receive them at all. Do you reject us utterly? I feel perhaps I

February 4th

I cannot remember what I meant to say, yesterday, so I start again (you see my strict use of paper has not changed). You may be pleased to know that your mother was up today for nearly two hours. I made her a long chair with a few blankets and the pillow from your bed. I brought out another chair and sat with her. It was very warm, and there were birds calling now and then—in February! The skin of her hand is as thin as silk now. I touched it while she slept. So your parents, hopelessly depraved, spent the afternoon. You may think on this.

your Father

February 7th

John Ephraim,

Today I rode to Rocky Ford myself. Some children on the street directed me out to the bank of the river, to a muddy place marked by hooves, where other people had come to look. The river went sliding along, very deep, so the surface spun slowly. There seemed to be no ice at all. Across, in the field, I saw the blue tent snapping in the warm wind above the winter grasses. The teetering skeleton of a fence encircled it, in some places ten feet high. Young boys were hammering boards and raw branches to the uprights. Under the crosspieces, children ran to and fro. One little girl dragged out a basket as big as a wheelbarrow, and began to pull it toward the water. A slender young man came out—my heart leapt, and fell—and took basket and child back inside. I stood until only a few blue triangles and the crackling blue roof were still visible to me. I turned to go.

Behind me a man stood on a tree stump. He was dressed like a farmer, with clumsy chunks of mud on his boots. He spoke down to me in an angry voice, and struck his own leg with his cap. He said, Who are they to build a bloody ark? As full of sin as the rest, and now living like that. A crime. And children with them. He said, They should be whipped.

It took me a long time to ride back to Broadhill, and Marie Spencer, who was looking after your mother, was late for her supper at home.

your Father

February 15th

John Ephraim,

Today I met James Spencer on the street and lifted my hand and smiled, and he went on past as though I'd been a phantom. I was so shaken. No explanation occurred to me at first. I went in at the feed-store and there was talking that hushed as the bell of the door died away. In the silence I bought twenty pounds of oats and had to pat my coat endlessly before I found money in its usual pocket.

Usually when I walk into the bank in the morning there is a flurry of industry at the desks; one can hear quills snap in earnestness. Today there was quiet, and a peering-round over shoulders. I sat in my chair and drew my papers toward me but I could not see. In a moment Satterwhite, James's clerk, came in to explain his absence. Addressing not me but the sleeve of my coat, he said that young Marie Spencer had left home on foot to go to the encampment at Rocky Ford, and had been gone all night before her parents caught up to her. They'd brought her back between them in the wagon and were seen by early risers. She spoke of your son, the clerk told me softly. So you see, John Ephraim, naturally the town has lunged to this repast of gossip. While you dally by the river, they feed on our good name.

At dusk, I walked over to the Spencers' place. I brooded on what could be done to quell the talk, to make the town forget you. It was one of the strange warm evenings we've been having, and I passed through the thin black trees of the woodlot, squinting into the last orange glint of the sun. Over my shoulder I saw that my shadow was as long as a path. Have you noticed, where you are, that though it is warm there are no new leaves?

Kit Spencer did not want to invite me in, I could see. But James motioned at the window. He offered me my usual chair and cup of tea.

When we had drunk, he said, Well, Josiah, she wants to be his wife in Heaven.

I tried to laugh a bit. He did not join me. He looked into the fire and rubbed his pinched nose. His face looked as it did years ago, when the river came up suddenly and drowned the lambs in their pen.

I have been wrong, he said, to trust his interest in her well-being.

Should I have said to him then what I had long hoped, that one day our children might love one another, and unite my family with that of my closest friend? I could not. I was afraid to see the impatient jerk of his face, the disdain. I stirred my tea.

He said, He has convinced her that the world will end and that he knows the day.

I said, It is the mad fervor of youth. It will pass. James, it must pass. But his face was set against me.

Then we saw young Marie at the door. Come through, my dear, said her father, and she came through the room without looking at me. If you are concerned for her, I will tell you: she looked much as usual, but tired. Her hair was escaping around her face and her red braid was rough and unruly behind. They have shown her that she must remain at home, James says. Twice, though, she has woken up weeping. She believes she will die by fire. For shame, John Ephraim. For shame.

your Father

February 24th

Dear John Ephraim,

You may have noticed that I have not written for some time. I had thought of remaining silent and letting curiosity bring you out. But I find there is too much to say to you. It is an empty house, with you gone, and your mother lying quietly abed. I find the space filling up with my thoughts. I build a stingy fire and, when your mother is sleeping, go down and deliberate beside it until it fades. I have been to Sunday services but twice since you went, preferring to worship at home with your mother. I'm not so pleased with this new man Wheelwright. He knows any amount of Scripture, but as for shedding light—he preaches hard on the thinnest verses, with much perspiring and waving of the elbows. In my evenings alone I have turned again to my Bible, and, I must say, have found much censure of your flight. The obvious I need not quote. We both know God's first direction to children, that their days might be long on the land. But do you ever chance to refresh your mind among the Psalms, and read: Rid me and deliver me from the hand of strange children, whose mouth speakest vanity, and their right hand is the hand of falsehood, that our sons may be as green plants grown up in their youth and our daughters may be as cornerstones? And Malachi, who writes that the heart of the children shall turn to the fathers lest the earth be smited with a curse. With these plain instructions and what natural love for us you may still bear, why do you stay away?

To be truthful I have also been reminded that it is not for a father to provoke his son to anger, and I have sat in reverie, considering it. After a week of such thinking I have decided this. That though your disrespect to your father is a clear sin, though your talk is humbug by his standard, though you have fled your family into a squalid delusion and corrupted the mind of a young girl—though these things be true without doubt in my mind, still I think I may have offended in my own small way. The afternoon before you went, when we spoke hotly near the barn, I implied that your mind was not your own. I saw you step back, brush in hand, from the sorrel who stood stamping and rippling her skin, but I continued as I felt I must. I did believe it was my duty to decide for you what might enrich or endanger your soul—you were my son, and still young, and living in my house. But when I shook your arm, and called you vain and dramatic, this may have hurt you. I acknowledge it.

Your mother requests that I come to you and ask you back. I cannot see my way to it just now. You must extend your own hand. But may this clear the air between us.

your Father

March 1st

John Ephraim,

For a week I've gone to the bank and concentrated only on that work. My regular hours, my usual dinner in the safety of friends. I've held conversations that never refer to my family. But at my desk I read. In the lectures and letters the papers print, I see that there is discussion of the 18th, 19th, and 20th days of this month, and of whether one must measure time by the time of day in Jerusalem. It is also said that in the encampments the people weave baskets in which they may sit and be whisked to heaven. It is the sneering writers who report this, I admit. I should think it general knowledge that if God wanted to take a man up He would not need to be provided with handles. I make these jokes to myself at my desk and then I lift my head and stare out into the street, and my heart pounds. Since James Spencer has given Marie leave to stay with your mother (though oh how coldly), I rode today to Rocky Ford.

The earth is hard under the drying decay of leaves; one can feel the shock of hooves against it. At the side of the road, poor bleached grasses wave. Some trees bear on their trunks a sleeve of grime, where ice was pooled only a few weeks past. The sun comes up strange, I think, with a light that looks very old, sharply yellow, biting at the eye. And yet nothing grows. Perhaps you have come out of your tent and seen this. The hatter says the weather is called a bright winter and, if one accepts the almanac, should precede an icy wet spring. I think of your tattered, disappointed tent, the rain thudding on you after the joyless great day.

The streets of Rocky Ford are also odd nowadays. They are dusty, and cheap newspapers are forever blowing about. The citizenry look furtive and exhausted. Occasionally I see a strange tight group of women moving along the walk. They carry baskets and buy flour and sugar in small supplies. I saw the storekeeper, the old one, sell a bag of sugar to a woman. He said, Let me sell you the ten pounds, since the price will be better, and looked at her with his face expectant. She laughed and said, No, sir, I thank you, but I buy sugar for this week, and next week, and the week after that. Then I'll have no need to sweeten the food on my table. When she went out, another woman, who had stood stock still and watched, went flying up to the old man and scolded him for selling at all to a wretched woman of the Blue

Tent. The old man's hoarse voice followed me out and was audible on the street.

Your mother had asked again that I go to see you. I went as far as the muddy place from which I watched before. Now the wall is high and sturdy. From where I stood I could see no gate. I did not go around to the ford to seek you. I am still waiting for you to make your choice.

your Father

March 2nd

John,

What I did not say yesterday. I heard a conversation that lowered my spirits. I had gone into the inn between Rocky Ford and Broadhill to drink a little wine and some tea. I thought I'd hear the politics, or about a new book to take home to your mother. But the place was crowded with laughing rabble, in for noon dinner. While I sat watching they hooted and slapped each other, and soon one stood up and called in a high, stern voice for all those at his table to be quiet.

Parson, they cried, Put down that beer, unseemly fellow!

Their friend shook his finger at them. Look here, you lot of ruined dogs, he said, still in this high voice like a woman's. Here's a prophecy.

The very word prophecy set them howling.

Then he said, I counted the sneezes of my cross-eyed goat and multiplied it by the seeds of a crooked-neck squash, and subtracted the freckles on the neck of my fat little bride! (A roar.)

How long did you count those freckles, sir? said one who wore a red cap.

Two days, said this parson, And carefully. You may be sure I'm in the right.

And what did you learn, brother? sang out another.

Blockhead! he said. The end of the world! Oh, then it was a merry table. One old fellow pushed back from the board and came over near me to rummage among bags on the floor.

The clever herd was clamoring for instruction. When must I be ready for the end? said the red cap.

No need, said the parson. It came and went the day you were born. The world coughed you up and then died.

Why, Parson, said one, soft and sly, That's no prophecy, then.

That's history.

The parson looked into his beer and said, It's prophecy in a looking glass.

It's Jesus don't know if he's coming or going, crowed the red cap. Much laughter.

So I been in hell and never knew the difference, said the sly one.

Here's the richest bit, said the parson, Those as went to Heaven never knew the difference either.

All stopped a minute and drank. The man at the bags stood near me, watching. Suddenly he turned to me and said, That's some bad nonsense, ain't it?

In my surprise I only nodded. He wiped his hands on his pants, and said, This is how you know it's a democracy. When you see fools free to believe in nothing.

And he took up his bags and went out.

While my attention was on him, the table had quieted. The men were at their food. One fellow, who had eyes skewed almost to the sides of his head, said gravely into the silence, I've got a stony soul or two to throw to that boy parson. I can pick them up off the ground, and throw them right to him. Let us see how quick his hands are.

From the table somewhere, Amen.

I confess I was concerned by this. The derision of the newspaper editors has given way to a savage rancor among the people.

Who is this boy parson, John Ephraim?

your Father

March 6th

John Ephraim,

Once I had a little boy, a sturdy gentle fellow, who crouched peering into the nests of grass fowl, and waited for hours at the lairs of small animals, until his knees were locked and painful and I had to work them with my hands. So where is my patient boy in the young man who demands his Lord come now to earth in his own lifetime? I wonder why the brightest young scholar I ever saw hold a slate should abnegate the future?

I have been thinking of you and what you must feel as you wait for the end. It's difficult. If I thought there would be no rough chain of days leading me onward, if I thought that the land I know, weedy, strewn with manure, camped upon by the vengeful obtuse race of man, if I believed it would all soon vanish in one flaming utterance of the holy, I should feel—grief. In your circumstance I could not muster joy. This in case you thought I might perhaps join you under the blue tent.

Marie Spencer has made supper for your mother and has just brought me apples and cheese. I watched her today as she brought water up the hill from the well. One moment she stopped to rest her pail on the ground, and the wind blew and pressed her dress back against her. The cat ran to her, and she picked it up and put it against her shoulder, and took up her pail and walked on. You are giving away forty years of sleep beside this girl. When this fever is off you, and you come back to look around, what will be left? The door is closing. The world and its doors. My son a gateless tabernacle. My wife a room growing darker.

Father

March 9th

John,

I go down the streets now with coat flapping and people stare. Your mother is worse. She is making preparations. How can you not come to her?

I hear her breathing all night. I hear her.

Father

March 14th

John Ephraim,

An ugly scene in Rocky Ford today. I am hardly recovered. I had gone over to the hatter's to hear the news, over those six miles that are so familiar now. The fields are densely matted, the shrubs bare and curling in the heat. Confused birds dart madly before and behind me as I ride. My winter clothes are heavy and I am wet inside them.

The hatter was not there. Business hours, mind you, and a Monday. The door was looped shut with a piece of rope. I could hardly believe it, but I knew what it meant. This dour and precise little man,

227

this ready scoffer, had abandoned his life. Strange that I should not have seen it coming, but I have overlooked before this what was placed in plain sight. Inside on the floor of the shop, I could see a man's silk hat. The crown was smashed flat. Beyond were others, treated likewise. I withdrew from this scene along the boardwalk, as if from the fatal spill of a runaway wagon. If the hatter is among you now I beg you do not tell him the hats are ruined. I consider him my friend, and hope to see him soon, back in his shop. I have known him for years, you know.

But it was more than this. As I came back along the street I saw two men standing some twenty feet apart from a woman I thought I knew, looking at her quite rudely. Other people were at their business all along the street, but they moved slow, slower, as though the spin of the earth were winding down like a clock. It was the woman who had bought such a small bag of sugar from the grocer a few weeks ago. She was not as gay, now, turning her shoulder to these men and tucking her chin down. Then—my God!—a stone rang on the iron ground, and skittered along under her skirt. The people listening moved slowly as lengthening shadows.

I rejoice, said the woman, I rejoice to be persecuted for the sake of the truth.

One rough laugh, a bray, floated down the street. The scene bore no resemblance to civilized life. I hurried into the breach between them, and took off my hat. Gentlemen, I called, look at yourselves.

I might have gone on but I saw that both victim and perpetrators had faded away. I was left standing alone, while the livid townspeople stumped past me across the baked and splintered storefronts. I still held my hat in my hand. I thought I heard someone breathe, Who does this old beggar think he is?

Were the people this way before you called them lost, John? Was kind company always a deep fraud, and the mild face of the land a harlot mask? The fence you have built has divided us, son from father. You have called us graceless, and we have plucked up that name and wear it.

I went home and sat by your mother; I sit there now as I write. She drinks a little water now and then. I feel severed even from her, by what I cannot describe. I can write only to you, who never respond, and who indeed may never hear me. I am tired now. The world doubles before me.

Father

March 16th

John,

I hurry to write because the post bag is leaving and I've detained the man at my desk. I think I will come to you the morning after. If you are willing, come out of there and down to the water to meet me.

Father

March 17th

Dear John,

Your great day approaches quickly. I have read that all expectations are now for the night of the 19th. Your mother wishes you well. That is all she will say.

Tonight I read to her from the naturalist's book about northern birds. She fell asleep suddenly, with her body twisted round and I sat there for a moment with my hand in the book, waiting to see if she would stir. Then suddenly I felt strongly that I must write to you. I thought, this is why the Lord is not coming. Not this year. Not the next. I was sure of it. (But why I should I feel so urgent to tell you why the end of the world is not coming, if the end of the world is not coming? I should have plenty of time.) It was this of which I thought, a story you may not know the whole of. Before your mother and I married, I worked at the bank to earn a home for us. She was waiting. But she had left school and was restless; she spent so much time reading books and seeing lectures that she was full of convictions. These led her to do work through her church down at Braxton. There's a house for the insane there, you know. Faithless, reasonless creatures, calling out like animals. I'd seen them. I was, I confess, against it.

But your mother went to them. She was with another girl; they were both eighteen. She sent me letters. In the mornings she washed their faces and bodies, and fed them by hand. The bedding was always foul and had to be washed nearly every day. Once she wrote me mourning for a white shirtwaist she'd made, that had become so torn, and so dirty with food and refuse, that she'd had to throw it away. But it was as though Providence had ruined her blouse, not people. She did not blame the mad, nor even mention them. In the afternoons, she read Scripture to a huddled group; the men were brought in and seated so they could listen. I remember her writing that Saint Francis had had easy work, preaching to birds. Her audience argued with her, or performed strange sudden dances, or repeated her words a half measure behind until she could hardly understand her own voice. On the terrible afternoon (she told me when I went down to fetch her) she was reading Psalms—some of the congregation were even asleep in their chairs—and one great sad boy stood up and began singing, and came forward and caught your mother up in his hands. He held her above his head, and she could see the floor turning and the cowering mad women crying. Then he threw her to the ground. Her back was hurt. That is why she has walked so poorly. And perhaps why she is sick now, still a woman in her prime.

I mean just that when I saw your mother sleeping in that twisted way, I think of what she gave, in pain and lost time, in lost work and sickness, to bring God to a place where there was no God. In hope that when she had worked to make earth holy, then God would see his place prepared, and return to us. But John Ephraim! You say God never blinked his distant white eye! That his vision is overcrusted with secret plans, and he will come to earth when it shall suit him, regardless of the extent of goodness, the number of saved. At his whim he will raze our land and purify it for his dwelling—a finer earth will suit him to dwell in, not the one he made long ago, a novice. No. Everything in me rebels at this, a Lord who averts his face from the like of your mother, who wraps his head in a cloak.

For years I have stood at evening on the rise next to Spencer's woodlot and heard every sound and smelled it all, and though the light fades my eyes are wider and wider open. Then I know a deer has come nosing among the brambles. I do not see her move but feel her there, her wiry fear and unconscious beauty. And by her that landscape is graced. Transformed by that black delicate hoof, the bone shin against which she rubs her face. So the landscape is more graceful for the work we may do, and God sees it. When we have brought all the deer out of the woods to stand in dark-eyed calm, then he will walk among us and feed us from his hand.

You may think I am too selfish an old fellow to speak of such progress. I am sure that I am selfish. But the finer earth must be partly of our making, John. I am sure of this also.

Father

Later. I find I cannot seal this letter without saying it. You have my love. My little boy.

Broadhill,
March 22nd

Dear Reverend Gearhart,

I thank you for your note of March 19th, and the uncollected letter. I am not surprised our letter carrier did not visit you as usual. As you know, it was a difficult morning for many people. I will tell you what I saw, if it will add anything for those who suffered. I went to the camp very early, while it was still night. I won't say I didn't watch the sky as I rode. The stars were weak up there. The nail holes in the tin of my lantern made more light. That night the cold descended—this bright weather has broken all over the state, I hear. It was a queer pleasure to see the deep frost form in the ditches, and the usual fingers of ice extend from the bank of the river. My horse slipped sharply once at the ford, and I had to get down and walk her. When I arrived at the camp, I looked back across the stream and saw the advancing day as a grayness among the trees.

A few people were camped under their wagons, asleep. Beyond them the enclosure looked huge and dark, but above it the tent could be seen, and a little light paled its blue roof. Inside the people were singing. The sound was melodious and brave but very soft. I wondered if some were dozing while others kept the watch, or if all were awake and the gray dawn was striking them, one by one, silent with despair. I stood listening, and my heart was turning inside me.

In the trees across the clearing there was motion. I peered, stopped, blew on my hands, widened my eyes again but could gather little light. I went over to my horse and put my hands under her blanket to warm them. In retrospect, I believe I saw the ruffians who started the fire. They must have crept up from the south side and there set the brush burning. They must have muffled their lanterns with cloths. If I had seen a glow I might have investigated. But how strange that I should have seen *no* light, that they should have been that stealthy.

The flames came quickly in the vegetation, dry under its frost. Those lying under wagons woke, ran to a small door in the wall, and began pounding upon it. I followed them, and pounded with my frozen hands. The singing separated into individual voices, then ceased. Behind me, my horse reared and tore at her reins. In a few moments the fire drove me back to her. I set her loose. She thumped into the ford, and I followed her, and others were on either side of me, carrying things—a gun, a bag of potatoes. They had abandoned their wagons. The fire was running along the ground, and twigs and branches were jerking and popping as though inspirited. The fence had turned a sweating dark brown, and the uprights were blackening. When the sun came up, that yellow light swallowed the flame, so it appeared, simply, that the air between us and the enclosure was deforming and wrinkling. I heard shouts and, somewhere, the ringing of an axe on wood. We stood dumbly across the water.

Well, it's as you know. Most came out through the new-cut door and scattered toward us, wailing, through the north-side trees. Eighteen were burned. A few went into the deep curve of the river and were lost.

My son was not among the living or the dead. Late in the day I walked on the smoldering site of the tent, which had burned and floated away in dark feathers that caught on the trees. I looked under the blankets at the wizened black figures. They had held their hands up at the approach of the fire, and still held them there in postures of fear, or praise. None were my boy. I walked along the river and found nothing. The ice had by then made a deep opaque ruffle along the bank. I suppose we will know little until the next thaw. There are others missing. Mine is not the only one. We may yet have peace of mind.

Thank you for asking after Nell. She continues. This, at least. But I look across a threshold always, into the place where I will live as a man alone. And you will be surprised to know of whom I am thinking, Reverend. It is the letter carrier who fills my mind. Yes, I know I have never met him.

You said he was about my age, perhaps older. I will be fifty soon. He was whiskered, and either drunk or longing to be drunk. But he always put the letters under his coat and touched his forehead respectfully. I can imagine him walking up to John Ephraim in the camp, saying, Here's another, and John opening it with his thin hands, and reading. I do not see his face, of course. To recollect the whole face is hard. I have only the feeling the face gave me. He puts the letters carefully between the leaves of his Bible. My letters make that Bible bristly and awkward to handle.

But if John were never there, or if this old man were a liar? Do you see what I am saying, Gearhart? The man takes the letters back to some room, and opens them with his yellow fingers. But the poor fellow cannot read. What was sent in faith he receives with confusion. Plea, argument, and lament are alike unintelligible to him. He touches the hieroglyphs with his fingers. He puzzles over my words in that high far room, he rubs the page against his sunken cheek and smears the ink. It falls from his hand. Already he has forgotten it. He goes to his window across a floor ankle-deep in letters. He treads on every undeciphered word.

If you have the time, Gearhart, I would like to come and see you. I would like to hear your voice.

Josiah Cole

Poems

I.

  The miners in the tunnels under the Atlantic stopped work and listened to the great boulders above rolling over the seabed.

II.

  The gull crying the great tune, which is the storm coming.

III.

  The tree lives inside its wooden fortress and the cherry blossom bursts out of the keep like banqueting light.

IV.

  Don't be shy about death, be an old man interested in it, like a virgin interested in sex.

V.

  To die, or to become invisible.

VI.

  His father dies, the son becomes more visible. He is the personification of death to the new generation. Because he has an invisible father, they are deferential to him, and he may very well grow a beard at this point.

VII.

  Can his father hear the rumbling of the boulder? Does he banquet with the light? Is he self-sufficient like the moon, mistress of self-propulsion?

VIII.

  Come into the old man's house before he leaves for ever. The air is cologned with happier drinking days, a fine Beaune reddened and tarred with age.

IX.

  Age is the only smell left after he leaves. Except for the smells of the water lilies meditating in the garden pond. That is an ageless smell.

X.

  I am breathing rather fast in this house of his papers. Into what word has the air stilled itself in the chambers of his skull?

XI.

  His darkened emission compares with my lighted one.

XII.

  I am shaken. I ask for a cup of tea. But it is his voice I hear. My tongue has his taste. The tea tastes of a matured tree.

XIII.

  Wisdom hath built herself a house, which if any man enter in, he shall be saved, and find pastures (Aurora Consurgens, *Parable 5*). But this home must be sold, having been cleaned of the effluvia of his last days, out of the curtains, out of the carpets, out of the paint work. We scrub and scrub until there is only a clean ghost-house left, with no occupant.

XIV.

  The bite-marks in the red apple turn it into a skull, slowly browning. Many old people have a post-mortem appearance. Is this his ghost, or have I dreamed of his death? Is he still dead when I awake?

XV.

      Beware lest the vinegar be turned unto smoke... How deep her clothing is, surrounded with variety. We had a wonderful Sunday walk by a new path to Maenporth, some days after the death. As we passed a cottage ruin that had extraordinarily thick walls, I said that I wished I could live in such fabrics, in the walls as well as the passageways.

Cornish Hills in the Black Mirror

Lumps of sulfur, like the Chinese oracle wrapped in yellow silk. Knowledge and anticipation. The dark glass cases in the museum alight with yellow sulfur-patches. Certain sunny gardens of crystal sulfur have been retired to these shelves of the Geological Museum. I read the cards and admire the Latin but watch for the life of these crystals lighting up my own interior museum. The powers that transmit energy from underground, controlling our ways, rest here in palpable colorful specimens, great nether bedrooms radiating post-coital peace. Flaming tar balls skim across the surfaces of clear underground lakes. Their shores are quivering quilts of mud, of shivering sand. The roomy Venusbergs, the ballrooms, sumps, latrines, halls, galleries, bedrooms—all stained in gorgeous swatches of ore, sometimes approaching the condition of landscape tapestry. The great copper bedrooms, the mile-long bedrooms of Venus. Staircases of quartz climbing to kitchens colored like beetroot with iron ore; wet tin ore silvering the precipices. Marshaling yards of recurrent caves, these caves traveling around unseen inside the hills, like escalators and lifts that can move in any direction. Think of the shed of an alchemist and the passageways of vapor between the massive units of equipment—that is the mountain with its caves winding, the gigantic alembics that distill and redistill the lime-freighted water and release it at last in laddering torrents out of sump-holes in sunny precipices, containing in liquid form the masonry and design of many cathedrals that will be laid down elsewhere as the water sinks, hollowing out the ground for its vaulted crypts. Indeed, the alchemist has become his work, only his beards remain—they rouse themselves in any piece of water that begins to move, that leaps off a rock in its dive. He is sheer play, which it was his purpose to become. He presides everywhere, transmitting the messages imprinted in his substance by the planets and the higher minerals which transduce the planetary influences and those of the stars, as do the gemstones' crystal points. As below, so above; he seeks to make a perfect model of the universe out of rocks and ores down below, so that the earth shall resonate the constellations in perfect rhythm.

It began with the mining which created an underground city as vast as the county. The magicians took over from the miners, and certain alchemists dissolved themselves into the rock, singing. You can see the crystal pattern of Merlin's beard inlaid on the wall of his esplumeor in the cave at Tintagel, the birth cave where the baby Arthur was found. Thus the world began to alter in its own way and become intelligible in Latin, however otherwise it might appear. There is praise below the rocks under the turf and many churches as they sing move up and down the roads and hills inside the rock, inside the black mountain with its floors moving up and down, with its doors opening and shutting like the true and veritable original of the ghost-house, with the heads popping out of secret paneling. The buses and charabancs driving to the ghost-house under the hill are churches on the move. The clouds above whiten with ice as they rise like refrigerated lifts, or descend, blushing with the warm rain that enters the ghost-house like fresh legions through innumerable pores. On certain days, every object, whether above ground or below it, becomes a fountain of ghost.

Manuduction

I.

The morning air sharp as reverse ether, that de-anesthetizes. Open shirt to open blouse—two lilies harkening to each other. The pollen of the chest, the balsam on the bosom, the bosom friends. The opening at the throat like the heart's white ear-trumpet. The frenulum of the garment, its little bridle where the cloth fastens, in him, right over left, in her, left over right. I am the only one afraid of these matters. However, this is what we see, as a preliminary to exchanging fluids in the name of God.

II.

A sculpture parkland sited on a Cornish cliff. "It was the great place you read about in books."

III.

The rock she picked up was sparkling with musicals, it glittered like theater curtains, it was a heavy tassel of the theater.

IV.

Entering by mistake the Ladies: waterhiss, a pleasant tang of cologne, a carpet on the floor, two vases of fresh flowers, and six small confessionals.

V.

The clouds hiss as they cross the view. They contain various transcendentals eager to drop on the visitor sheltering beneath the pines.

VI.

Honest, rational clothing, dispensable. The love bites like a ring o' roses.

Roden Crater

I n 1974, James Turrell developed a plan to use the form of a volcano and its surroundings to order and heighten perception of the material and temporal presence of natural light. His idea was to demonstrate that an observer standing on an open plain experiences "celestial vaulting"—he senses that the sky is not limitless, it has a definable shape and encloses the space below it—and that, when the observer lies down, he can grasp a curvilinear sensation of the space of the sky.

Turrell began searching for a hemispherically-shaped, dished space, four hundred to a thousand feet above a plain. A high-altitude site would reveal the slight convex curvature of the earth, which pilots flying at low altitude can often experience. Infrequent cloud cover was also desirable, so that the deeper blue of the sky could support the sense of enclosed celestial vaulting an observer would experience from the bottom of the crater.

After flying over all the Western states, looking for possible sites, Turrell selected Roden Crater, a volcano on the edge of the Painted Desert near Flagstaff, in northeastern Arizona, and began work on what has become his monumental work-in-progress, the Roden Crater Project. While much of the geological form of the crater remains untouched, some aspects have been altered to enhance the viewer's perception of daily and seasonal astral events. For example, a 1,035-foot long semicircular, arched tunnel 8 ½ feet in diameter has been dug through the wall of the crater and aligned to frame the southernmost moonset.

Through his extensive topographical maps and a series of site photographs, Turrell has chronicled the changing aspects of this grand aesthetic engineering project and contrasted human solipsism with that of an indifferent universe.

Roden Crater, Aerial View, 1975–present.

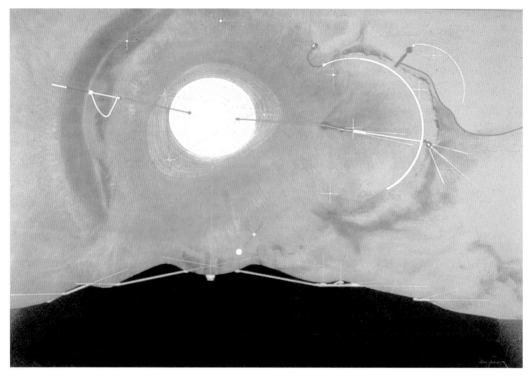

Roden Crater Site Plan with Projected Cross Section, 1990.

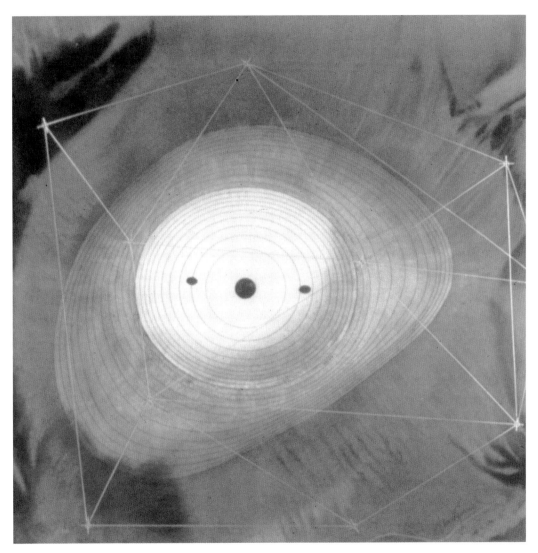

Roden Crater Bowl, Finished Contours, 1990.

Roden Crater, Cut and Fill Topo.

Roden Crater with the Typical Cumulus Clouds of the August Monsoon Season.

Roden Crater with Wind-drifted Snow.

Roden Crater at Sunset Just Before the Earth's Shadow Covers It.

Letters, young and old poets

Truro
Nov. 29

And when you despaired, what sustained you?

•

Directed. Directive: you ask. I am a slow
learner. Coming around corners the dilemma,
a shrinking light they put before me.
A melodrama when I tell you half.
The edge of the seat thing: nausea in the lap of memory,
presently a soft look comes over me.

Today is someone's birthday.
On this day I do nothing to hurt
anybody. Sites of exquisite communion
observed. A perfect word replaced. Oh spill the milk,

spill the milk again.
Vanity. Favoritism. Strong curtain
fluttering for rent. I must travel
far in excess. Back to the graveyard,

all part and parcel, wreathed in smiles.
Such child-bearing going on between these portals.
Remember the smell of a fairy-ring crushed,

"Aux mortes." Towards grass
and any young rabbit crushed in it. Conspirators,
I just heard of *duende.* Oh give me a home...

•

Sagres
April 24th

Do you really? I can't feel it.

•

Nothing came to replace the devil
in my heart. A paltry vivacity.
Even in my weakened state
I change this place that's been the same
fifty-odd years. Clumsy, lurching,
like a monster. But like a monster I'm working
my way towards you. I reject lightheartedness
temporarily: I will not whore myself.
There is actually something wrong with me.
The smell of paint saves it. Industry,
slapping something white on the old wall.

•

Glasgow
Tuesday the 25th

Who are these animals that I entertain?

•

I could be alone when instead I am with them,
there were parts of me they liked. A quorum
compromising. Bald statement issuing from the first
layer, pre-lapsarian, everything so easeful
it erases its

Back to not understanding. It's rich,
the story of my phantom containment: a small,
modernized garret.

I sleep well in the colder air.
Memories of the seminary—any tight space.

•

Roma
Wednesday, November 26th

Darling, sweetheart. When?

•

Trust a reconstructed mind to resist
the impulse. One is surviving when
resisting. Swallowing benign death
in immature silence.

Weather on top.
Stupid but not evil,
inside and outside, in the service.
Events appear to conspire.
A struggle to keep up my end.

Beneficence

I had inherited the studio from a photographer. A lilac-hued canvas still stood by the wall, depicting part of a balustrade and a whitish urn against the background of an indistinct garden. And it was in a wicker armchair, as if on the very threshold of those gouache depths, that I sat, thinking of you, until morning. It got very cold at daybreak. Roughcast clay heads gradually floated out of the murk into the dusty haze. One of them (your likeness) was wrapped in a wet rag. I traversed this hazy chamber—something crumbled and crackled underfoot—and, with the end of a long pole, hooked and pulled open in succession the black curtains that hung like shreds of tattered banners across the slanting glass. Having ushered in the morning—a squinty, wretched morning—I started laughing, and had no idea why; perhaps it was simply because I had spent the entire night sitting in a wicker armchair, surrounded by rubbish and shards of plaster of Paris, amid the dust of congealed plasticine, thinking of you.

Here is the kind of feeling I would experience whenever your name was mentioned in my presence: a bolt of black, a scented, forceful motion—that's how you threw back your arms when adjusting your veil. Long had I loved you; why, I know not—with your deceitful, savage ways, dwelling as you did in idle melancholy.

Recently I had come across an empty matchbox on your bedside table. On it there was a small funereal mound of ashes and a golden cigarette butt—a gold, masculine one. I implored you to explain. You laughed unpleasantly. Then you burst into tears and I, forgiving everything, embraced your knees and pressed my wet eyelashes to the warm black silk. After that I did not see you for two weeks.

The autumn morning shimmered in the breeze. I carefully stood the pole in a corner. The tiled roofs of Berlin were visible through the window's broad span, their outlines varying with the iridescent inner irregularities of the glass; in their midst, a distant cupola rose like a bronze watermelon. The clouds were scudding, rupturing, fleetingly revealing an astonished, gossamer, autumnal blue.

The day before I had spoken to you on the phone. It was I who had given in and called. We agreed to meet today at the Brandenburg gate. Your voice, through the bee-like hum, was remote and anxious. It kept sliding into the distance and vanishing. I spoke to you with tightly shut eyes, and felt like crying. My love for you was the throbbing, welling warmth of tears. That is exactly how I imagined Paradise: silence and tears, and the warm silk of your knees. This you could not comprehend.

After dinner, when I went outside to meet you, my head began to whirl from the crisp air and the torrents of yellow sunlight. Every ray echoed in my temples. Large, rustling, russet leaves waddled as they raced along the sidewalk.

I reflected while I walked that you would probably not come to the rendezvous. And that, if you did, we would quarrel again anyway. I knew only how to sculpt and how to love. This was not enough for you.

The massive gates. Wide-hipped buses squeezing through the portals and rolling down the boulevard, which receded into the restless blue glitter of the windy day. I waited for you under an oppressive vault, between chilly columns, near the grate of the guardhouse window. People everywhere: Berlin clerks were leaving their offices, ill-shaven, each with a briefcase under his arm and, in his eyes, the torpid nausea that comes when you smoke a bad cigar on an empty stomach—their weary, predatory faces, their high starched collars, flashed by endlessly; a woman passed with a red straw hat and a gray caracole coat; then a youth in velvet pants buttoned under the knees; and others still.

I waited, leaning on my cane, in the cold shadow of the corner columns. I did not believe you would come.

By one of the columns, near the guardhouse window, was a stand with postcards, maps, fan-spreads of colored photos, and by it, on a stool, sat a brown little old woman, short-legged, plump, with a round, speckled face, and she too was waiting.

I wondered which of us would wait longer, and who would come first—a customer, or you. The old woman's mien conveyed something like this: "I just happen to be here... I sat down for a minute ...Yes, there's some kind of stand nearby, with excellent, curious knickknacks... But I have nothing to do with it..."

People passed ceaselessly between the columns, skirting the corner of the guardhouse; some glanced at the postcards. The old woman would tense every nerve and fix her bright tiny eyes on the passerby, as if transmitting a thought: buy it, buy it... but the other, after a quick survey of the colored cards and the gray ones, walked on, and she, with seeming indifference, lowered her eyes and went back to the red book she was holding in her lap.

I did not believe you would come. But I waited for you as I had never waited before, smoking restlessly, peeking beyond the gate toward the uncluttered plaza at the start of the boulevard; then I would retreat anew into my nook, trying not to give the appearance of waiting, trying to imagine that you were walking, approaching while I was not looking, that if I took another peek around the corner I would see your seal-fur coat and the black lace hanging from your hat rim down over your eyes—and I deliberately did not look, cherishing the self-deception.

There was a rush of cold wind. The woman got up and started pushing her postcards more firmly into their slots. She wore a kind of yellow plush jacket with gathers at the waist. The hem of her brown skirt was hiked up higher in front than in back, which made her look as if she were thrusting out her belly when she walked. I could make out meek, kind-hearted creases on her round little hat and her worn duck bootees. She was busily arranging her tray of wares. Her book, a guide to Berlin, lay on the stool, and the autumn wind absently turned the pages and ruffled the map that had fallen from them like a flight of stairs.

I was getting cold. My cigarette smoldered lopsidedly and bitterly. I felt the waves of a hostile chill on my chest. No customer had appeared.

Meanwhile the knickknack woman got back on her perch and, since the stool was too tall for her, she had to do some squirming, with the soles of her blunt bootees leaving the sidewalk by turns. I tossed away the cigarette and flicked it with the end of my cane, provoking a fiery spray.

An hour had passed already, maybe more. How could I think you would come? The sky had imperceptibly turned into one continuous storm cloud, the passersby walked even faster, hunched over, holding onto their hats, and a lady who was crossing the square opened her umbrella as she went. It would be a real miracle if you were to arrive now.

The old woman had meticulously placed a marker in her book and paused as if lost in thought. My guess is she was conjuring up a rich foreigner from the Adlon Hotel who would buy all her wares, and overpay, and order more, many more picture postcards and guidebooks of all kinds. And she probably was not very warm either in that velour jacket. You had promised you would come. I remembered the phone call, and the fleeting shadow of your voice. God, how I wanted to see you. The ill wind started gusting again. I turned up my collar.

Suddenly the window of the guardhouse opened, and a green soldier hailed the old woman. She quickly scrambled down from her stool and, with her thrust-out belly, scuttled up to the window. With a relaxed motion, the soldier handed her a steaming mug and closed the sash. His green shoulder turned and withdrew into the murky depths.

Gingerly carrying the mug, the woman returned to her seat. It was coffee with milk, judging by the brown fringe of skin sticking to the rim.

Then she began drinking. I have never seen a person drink with such utter, profound, concentrated relish. She forgot her stand, the postcards, the chill wind, her American client, she just sipped, sucked, disappeared totally into her coffee—exactly as I forgot about my vigil and saw only the velour jacket, the bliss-dimmed eyes, the stubby hands clutching the mug in their woolen mittens. She drank for a long time, drank in slow swallows, reverently licking off the fringe of skin, heating her palms on the warm tin. And a dark, sweet warmth poured into my soul. My soul, too, was drinking and heating itself, and the brown little woman tasted of coffee with milk.

She finished. For a moment she paused, motionless. Then she rose and headed for the window to return the mug.

But she stopped halfway, and her lips gathered into a little smile.

She scuttled rapidly back to her stand, snatched up two colored postcards, and, hurrying back to the iron grille of the window, softly tapped on the glass with her small woolly fist. The grille opened, a green sleeve glided out, with a gleaming button on the cuff, and she thrust mug and cards into the dark window with a series of hasty nods. The soldier, examining the photographs, turned away into the interior, slowly shutting the sash behind him.

Here I became aware of the world's tenderness, the profound beneficence of all that surrounded me, the blissful bond between me and all of creation, and I realized that the joy I had sought in you was not only secreted within you, but breathed around me everywhere, in the speeding street sounds, in the hem of a comically lifted skirt, in the metallic yet tender drone of the wind, in the autumn clouds bloated with rain. I realized that the world does not represent a struggle at all, or a predaceous sequence of chance events, but shimmering bliss, beneficent trepidation, a gift bestowed on us and unappreciated.

And at that instant you arrived at last—or, rather, not you but a German couple, he in a raincoat, legs in long stockings like green bottles; she slender and tall, in a panther coat. They approached the stand, the man began selecting, and my little old coffee woman, flushed, puffed up, looked now into his eyes, now at the cards, fussing, moving her eyebrows tensely like an old cabbie urging on his nag with his whole body. But the German had barely had time to pick something out when, with a shrug of her shoulder, his wife tugged him away by the sleeve. It was then I noticed that she resembled you. The similarity was not in the features, not in the clothes, but in that squeamish, unkind grimace, in that cursory, indifferent glance. The two of them walked on without buying anything, and the old woman only smiled, replaced her postcards in their slots, and again became absorbed in her red book. There was no point in waiting any longer. I departed along darkening streets, peering into the faces of passersby, capturing smiles and amazing little motions—the bobbing of a girl's pigtail as she tossed a ball against a wall, the heavenly melancholy reflected in a horse's purplish, oval eye. I captured and collected all of it. The oblique, plump raindrops grew more frequent, and I recalled the cool coziness of my studio, the muscles, foreheads, and strands of hair that I had modeled, and felt in my fingers the subtle tingle of my thought starting to sculpt.

It grew dark. The rain was gusting. The wind greeted me turbulently at every corner. Then a streetcar clanged past, its windows agleam with amber, its interior filled with black silhouettes. I hopped aboard as it passed and began drying my rain-soaked hands.

The people in the car looked sullen and swayed sleepily. The black windowpanes were specked with a multitude of minute raindrops, like a night sky overcast with a beadwork of stars. We were clattering along a street lined with noisy chestnut trees, and I kept imagining that the humid boughs were lashing the windows. And when the tram halted one could hear, overhead, the chestnuts plucked by the wind knocking against the roof. Knock—then again, resiliently, gently: knock, knock. The tram would chime and start, the gleam of the streetlamps shattered in the wet glass, and, with a sensation of poignant happiness, I awaited the repetition of those meek, lofty sounds. The brakes slammed on for a stop. Again a round, solitary chestnut dropped, and, after a moment, another thumped and rolled along the roof: knock, knock...

Translated from the Russian by Dmitri Nabokov

CONTRIBUTORS

Vito Acconci, with Acconci Studio (Luis Vera, Jenny Schrider, Charles Doherty), works on architecture and landscape. Their recent public projects include a plaza in front of the English Department building at Queens College, New York, a courtyard for an elementary school in the Bronx, New York, a public garden between two private gardens in Brooklyn, New York. They are currently working on a transportation center in Scottsdale, Arizona, and a city center in Chenove, France. The notes that accompany his portfolio are adapted from his longer article *Making Public: The Writing and Reading of Public Space* (Stroom, The Hague, 1993).

John Ashbery's most recent collection of poetry is *Can You Hear, Bird* (Farrar, Straus & Giroux).

Mel Bochner was born in Pittsburgh, Pennsylvania in 1940. In October, an exhibition devoted to his early work *Mel Bochner: Thought Made Visible* (1966–1973) will open at the Yale University Art Museum in New Haven. Bochner lives and works in New York City, where he is represented by Sonnabend Gallery.

William S. Burroughs is the author of *Naked Lunch, Queer, Junky, The Western Land, The Cat Inside, My Education: A Book of Dreams*, and the forthcoming *Ghost of Chance* (High Risk/Serpent's Tail) from which the passage in *Grand Street* is excerpted. He is a member of the American Academy and Institute of Art and Letters. He lives in Lawrence, Kansas.

Michael Carlson was born in New Haven, Connecticut and lives in London where he works as a freelance journalist and as the commentator on Sky Sports for the World League of American Football. His poetry has appeared in *Origin, The Mississippi Review, Scripsi*, and *Hollands Maanbladt* among others. His collections include *Chump Change* (Northern Lights) and *Zombie Footwork* (Hardpressed).

Douglas Cooper's first novel, *Amnesia*, was published by Hyperion and shortlisted for the Commonwealth Prize. His feature screenplay, *The Arm of the Carnivore*, will be directed this fall by Gavin Millar and produced by Talisman Films. Cooper collaborated with architects Diller & Scofidio on a virtual reality installation for the Pompidou Center in Paris and will be Peter Eisenman's partner on a project for the Milan Triennale. The story published here is excerpted from *Delirium*, the first novel to be serialized on the World Wide Web. Cooper can be reached on the Web at (http://www.timeinc.com/~twep/Features/Delirium/DelTitle.html).

CONTRIBUTORS

Sándor Csoóri, a leading contemporary Hungarian poet, essayist, and scriptwriter, has been one of the most prominent artistic spokespersons for the Hungarian people over the past four decades. The author of numerous volumes of poetry and essays, he has received the Attila József Prize in poetry and the prestigious Kossuth Award, Hungary's highest honor for achievement in artistic or scientific work. A founder and major figure in the Hungarian Democratic Forum since its inception, Csoóri has also worked to ensure the rights of ethnic Hungarians in other countries. His *Selected Poems* (Copper Canyon Press), translated by Len Roberts, was published in 1992.

Moyra Davey works in New York City, where she is represented by American Fine Arts, Co. She is originally from Montreal.

Emani Joma Gaynes Davis was born in Albany, New York in 1978 and, in 1980, moved with her mother to Takoma Park, Maryland, where she attended Sidwell Friends School. She later attended public schools in Brooklyn, White Plains, and Hastings-on-Hudson, New York. She will graduate from high school in 1997, and hopes to pursue a college education and career in psychology.

Cleveland Jomo Davis was born in Enfield, North Carolina in 1942, and moved to Virginia Beach, Virginia in 1954. The oldest of six children, he served his first prison sentence in 1961. Ten years later, he was incarcerated at Attica, where he was a Black Panther leader, and was indicted as one of the Attica Brothers after the 1971 rebellion. In 1976, he married Elizabeth Gaynes, with whom he has two children, Emani and Ari. In 1985, he was sentenced to 122 years for burglary and felony murder. He is currently imprisoned in Virginia.

Rachel Blau DuPlessis's most recent poems have appeared in *Hambone, Common Knowledge, Chelsea, Action Poetique,* and *The Gertrude Stein Awards Anthology* (Sun & Moon Press).

Elizabeth Gaynes was born in New York City in 1947 and was raised in Hastings-on-Hudson, New York. She received a B.A. from Syracuse University in 1968 and a law degree in 1972. She is currently the executive director of the Osborne Association, a nonprofit criminal justice organization that provides services to prisoners, former prisoners, and their families. During her twelve years at Osborne, she has developed several innovative program models, including a parenting program for incarcerated fathers.

Alberto Giacometti was born in Borgonovo, Swizerland in 1901. He studied from 1919 to 1920 at the School of Arts and Crafts, Geneva, and then in Paris at the Académie de la Grande-Chaumière, under Bourdelle, who was a student of Rodin's, from 1922 to 1925. He became a member of the Surrealist Group in 1925, but was "excommunicated" in 1934. During the '30s, he experimented with sculptures with movable parts, and, from 1940 to 1945, he reduced the scale of his work, to produce figures that were only an inch high. In 1945, he began working on full-scale figures again, but found that he could only "get a resemblance" when they were very thin. From then on, Giacometti worked in a strictly figurative vein, and turned also to graphic, almost monochromatic paintings. His work at this time embodied a melancholic, pared-down account of humanity. In 1953, he designed the original stage sets for Samuel Beckett's *Waiting for Godot.* Giacometti died in Paris in 1966.

Gerald Heard was born in London in 1889, and spent his youth in the agricultural cooperative movement in Ireland (where his family has been part of the "landed gentry" since the sixteenth century). He studied history at Cambridge University and worked as a BBC science commentator during the early days of radio. He lectured on ethics and metaphysics at Oxford University and became a member of the council of the Psychological Research Society. At 48, Heard moved to Los Angeles and conducted a regular lecture series at Hollywood's Vedanta Temple. He wrote numerous books on metaphysics, religion, and science fiction. He died in 1971. His book *Is Another World Watching* (Harper's Brothers) was published in 1950. The piece that appears here is excerpted from an article printed in *Fortnight*, August 17, 1953.

Matt Jasper washes dishes in a restaurant owned by his wife and ex-wife in Dover, New Hampshire. He is a frequent contributor to *Roller Derby* and *The Flat Earth Society* newsletter.

Jasper Johns was born in Augusta, Georgia, in 1930. In 1958, the Leo Castelli Gallery, New York, held his first one-person exhibition; eleven other shows followed, and were celebrated in 1993 with the retrospective exhibition *Jasper Johns: 35 Years with Leo Castelli.* The Museum of Modern Art, New York, is currently organizing a retrospective of Johns's work to open in the fall of 1996. Johns divides his time between his studios in New York City, Connecticut, and the French West Indies.

Rodney Jones's fifth book of poetry *Things That Happen Once* will be published by Houghton Mifflin in the spring of 1996. He teaches at Southern Illinois University in Carbondale.

Anna Keesey was raised in Oregon. She is a former high school teacher, a graduate of the creative writing program at the University of Iowa, and was recently a fellow at the Fine Arts Work Center in Provincetown, Massachusetts. She now holds a James Michener/Copernicus Society Fellowship.

Elias Khoury is the editor-in-chief of the literary supplement of *An-Nahar*, Beirut's principal newspaper and the artistic director of the Théâtre de Beirut. He is the author of several novels, three of which—*Little Mountain, Gates of the City*, and *The Journey of Little Gandhi*—have been translated into English and published by the University of Minnesota Press.

Jane Kramer writes the "Letter from Europe" for *The New Yorker*. Her last book was *Europeans* (Farrar, Straus & Giroux) and her next will be a collection of pieces from Germany (forthcoming from Random House). She lives in Paris and New York.

Anette Marta is a secondary school teacher and administrator in Pecs, Hungary.

W. S. Merwin was born in New York City in 1927. His collections of poetry and prose include *The Lost Upland, Travels, The Rain in the Trees*, and *The Carrier of Ladders*, for which he was awarded the Pulitzer Prize in 1970. His new collection of poems, *The Vixen*, will be published by Alfred A. Knopf.

Margaret Morton, a documentary photographer who lives in New York City, is an associate professor of art at the Cooper Union School of Art. Since 1989 she has photographed the dwellings that New York's homeless individuals create for themselves. Morton's photographs from *Fragile Dwelling* are on exhibition at the National Building Museum, Washington, DC until November 1995, and at the Triennale in Milan and the Kunstverein in Hamburg through mid-October. Her book, *The Tunnel*, will be published by Yale University Press in October 1995. Photographs from *The Tunnel* will be exhibited at Lowinsky Gallery, New York City, in the fall of 1995. Morton is the co-author of *Transitory Gardens, Uprooted Lives* (Yale University Press).

Dmitri Nabokov, the son of Vladimir Nabokov, was born in Berlin in 1934 and came to the United States as a child. He graduated from Harvard, served in the U.S. Army, and then began the vocal studies that led him to become an opera and concert performer. He has translated most of his father's Russian short stories and plays and many of his novels into English.

Vladimir Nabokov was born in St. Petersburg in 1899. He graduated from Trinity College, Cambridge, and moved to the United States in 1940. He died in Switzerland in 1977. The story *Beneficence* will appear in *The Stories of Vladimir Nabokov* (edited by Dmitri Nabokov), to be published by Alfred A. Knopf, in October 1995.

Joachim Neugroschel, who has won three PEN Translation Prizes and the translation prize of the French-American Foundation, has translated 150 books, including works by Paul Celan and Georges Bataille, as well as Nobel laureates Elias Canetti and Albert Schweitzer.

Steven Pippin is a sculptor and photographer who lives and works in London.

Peter Redgrove studied science at Cambridge and has worked as a research scientist and scientific journalist. He also trained as a lay analyst with John Layard, one of Jung's students. He has published twenty-three volumes of poetry and is considered to be one of Britain's leading poets. He has also published nine novels and had four of his plays performed.

Len Roberts's most recent books of poems are *Counting the Black Angels* (University of Illinois Press) and *Dangerous Angels* (Copper Beach). Copper Canyon Press published his translation of Sándor Csoóri's *Selected Poems* in 1992. Roberts was a Fulbright Scholar in Hungary in 1988 and a Fulbright Translator there in 1991.

Charles Simic is the author of seventeen collections of poetry, four books of prose, and numerous translations. He has won many awards, including a MacArthur Fellowship and a Pulitzer Prize. His new collection of poems, *Wedding in Hell*, was published by Harcourt Brace.

Hugh Steinberg has had work published in *Grand Street* and *The Indiana Review*. He has work forthcoming in *Puerto del Sol* and *Synesthetic*. He lives in Chicago, where he is a volunteer for the Guild Complex.

Kip S. Thorne is the Feynman Professor of Theoretical Physics at the California Institute of Technology in Pasadena, and is the author of the prize-winning book *Black Holes and Time Warps: Einstein's Outrageous Legacy* (W.W. Norton, 1994).

James Turrell was born in Los Angeles, California in 1943. His recent solo exhibitions include those held at the Barbara Gladstone Gallery, New York, the Hayward Gallery, London, the Institute of Contemporary Art, Philadelphia, the Wiener Secession, Vienna, and the Museum of Modern Art, New York. Turrell became a Chevalier des Arts et des Lettres in 1991, a MacArthur Foundation Fellow in 1984, and a Guggenheim Fellow in 1974. A retrospective of his work will be shown at Art Tower Mito, Ibaraki, Japan in November 1995. He lives and works in Flagstaff, Arizona.

Robert Venturi, with partner Denise Scott Brown, has had a decisive influence on architects throughout the world. His book, *Complexity and Contradiction in Architecture*, first published in 1966, has been translated and published in sixteen different languages. He has received numerous awards, including the National Medal of Arts, and is a member of the American Academy of Arts and Letters and a Fellow of the American Institute of Architects and the American Academy of Arts and Sciences. *Evocation and Iconography in Architecture For Generic Buildings Defined by Electronic Technology: A Series of Essays Reflecting a View from the Drafting Room and Aphorisms Galore*, the collection of writings from which the aphorisms printed in *Grand Street* are excerpted, will be published by MIT Press in February 1996.

Ivan Vladislavić was born in Pretoria in 1957. After studying at the University of the Witwatersrand, he worked as an editor at Ravan Press in South Africa. He has been publishing short fiction since the early '80s and his work has appeared in *The Bloody Horse*, the *English Academy Review*, *Staffrider*, and *TriQuarterly*, among others. *The Folly*, a novel published by David Philip in South Africa and Serif in the United Kingdom, won the CNA Literary Award for 1993. *The Box* is excerpted from his collection *Missing Persons* (David Philip, South Africa), which received the Olive Schreiner Prize in 1991.

Alissa Walser was born in Vienna in 1961. She studied painting in New York and Vienna, and has translated plays from the English to German. She was awarded the Ingeborg Bachmann Prize in 1992 and *Dies ist nicht meine ganze Geschichte*, the story collection from which *His Wedding* was excerpted and translated, was published in Germany by Rowohlt. She lives and works in Frankfurt, Germany.

Mark Weiss has taught writing and literature at Columbia University, Hunter College, Pima College, the University of Arizona, and the University of California at San Diego. He has published two chapbooks, *A Letter to Maxine* (Heron Press) and *A Block-Print by Kuniyoshi* (Four Zoas/Nighthouse Press), and two collections of poetry, *Intimate Wilderness* (New River Press) and *Fieldnotes* (Junction Press). Originally from New York, Weiss currently lives in San Diego, where he deals in fine art. *Painted* is from a work in progress.

Irvine Welsh is the author of *The Acid House* (Jonathan Cape/W.W. Norton), *Trainspotting* (Secker & Warburg), and *The Marabou Stork Nightmares* (to be published by W.W. Norton in February 1996), from which *Another Lost Empire* is excerpted. He lives in Amsterdam.

Rebecca Wolff lives in Truro, Massachusetts. Her work has appeared in *The Iowa Review, The Colorado Review,* and *Mudfish*. She is a graduate of the Iowa Writers' Workshop.

Barbara Wright has won the Scott Moncrieff Translation Prize three times. The authors whose work she has translated include Raymond Queneau, Robert Pinget, Nathalie Sarraute, Pierre Albert-Birot, Patrick Modiano, and Michel Tournier.

ILLUSTRATIONS

front cover Jasper Johns, *Untitled* (detail), 1993. Watercolor on paper, 40⅞ x 27⅝ in. Copyright Jasper Johns/VAGA, New York, 1995. Photograph copyright Jim Strong Inc. Courtesy of the artist and Leo Castelli Gallery.

back cover Vito Acconci, *Proposal for Klapper Hall, Queens College, New York, 1993–1995.* Fiberglass, granite finish, light, 60 x 80 x 160 ft. Courtesy of the artist and Barbara Gladstone Gallery, New York.

title page Mel Bochner, *If At Every Moment The Arrow Is At Rest, When Does It Move?* (detail), 1992. Oil on canvas, 98 x 98 in. Courtesy of Sonnabend Gallery, New York.

pp. 25–32 Vito Acconci, *Parks, Streets, and Vehicles.* Titles, dates, and captions appear with illustrations. Courtesy of the artist and Barbara Gladstone Gallery, New York, except **p. 28 (bottom)** copyright Paul Warchol, New York, 1993. **p. 25** Aluminum rowboats, soil, grass, trees, 10 x 12 x 36 ft. **pp. 26–27** Truck tractor and flatbed, corrugated galvanized steel, grating, chain, 13 x 22 x 130 ft. **p. 28** Supra-board, plaster, steel, plywood, hinges, 9 x 100 x 14 ft. **p. 29** Fiberglass, granite finish, light, 60 x 80 x 160 ft. **p. 30** Fiberglass with granite surface, 4'11" x 196'10" x 9'10". **pp. 31–32** Aluminum, steel, grating, lights, water, trees, ground-cover, 30 x 88 x 322 ft.

pp. 54–61 Margaret Morton, *Fragile Dwelling.* Eight black-and-white photographs, 8 x 10 in. each. Courtesy of the artist. Titles, dates, and captions appear with illustrations.

pp. 73–80 Jasper Johns, *Works on Paper.* Titles, dates, media, and dimensions appear on **p. 72.** Copyright Jasper Johns/VAGA, New York, 1995. **p. 73, p. 74,** and **pp. 78–79** Photographs copyright Dorothy Zeidman. **p. 76** Photograph copyright Douglas M. Parker, courtesy of Gemini G.E.L., Los Angeles. **p. 76** and **p. 80** Courtesy of Universal Limited Art Editions, West Islip, New York. **p. 77** Photograph copyright Jim Strong Inc. Courtesy of the artist and Leo Castelli Gallery, New York.

pp. 100–101, p. 102 (top and inset), p. 103 (top), and **p. 104** Photographs courtesy of Bettmann. **p. 103 (bottom), p. 105 (main photograph and inset)** Photographs courtesy of AP/Wide World Photos.

pp. 110–126 Black-and-white and color photographs courtesy of Elizabeth Gaynes.

pp. 130–135 Moyra Davey, *Newsstands.* Titles and dates appear with illustrations. Six Ektacolor prints, 10 x 10 in. each. Courtesy of American Fine Arts, Co., New York.

pp. 156–163 Mel Bochner, *All Parallels Converge At Infinity.* Titles and dates appear with illustrations. Courtesy of Sonnabend Gallery, New York. **p. 156** Chalk on paper, 25½ x 38 in. **p. 157** Oil on canvas, 48 x 72 in. **p. 158** Oil on canvas, 72 x 48 in. **p. 159** Oil on canvas, 96 x 36 in. **p. 160** Oil on canvas, 80 x 30 in. **p. 161, p. 162** and **p. 163** Oil on canvas, 98 x 98 in.

p. 164 Illustration by Matt Zimet.

pp. 177–183 Steven Pippin, *The Continued Saga of an Amateur Photographer.* **p. 177** Equipment valise. **pp. 178–179** Video stills taken from the film *The Continued Saga of an Amateur Photographer,* color and sound, 22 minutes. **pp. 180–181** and **pp. 182–183** Photographic paper positives, contact-printed from the original paper negatives, exposure time 1½ minutes, dimensions 18 x 23 in. each. Courtesy of Gavin Brown's enterprise, New York.

pp. 204–211 Photographs courtesy of AP/Wide World Photos.

pp. 241–248 James Turrell, *Roden Crater.* **pp. 241–247** Drawings and photographs by James Turrell, **p. 247** Photograph by Dick Wiser, 1986. Courtesy of the artist and Barbara Gladstone Gallery, New York.

pp. 266 Collage by Matt Jasper.

The artwork on page 270, of issue 53, was part of artist Pam Butler's *The Win Project,* 1995.

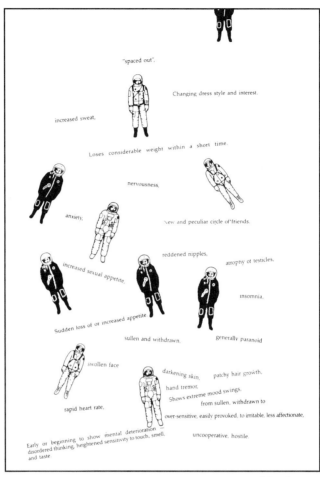

Matt Jasper

Grand Street would like to thank
the following for their generous support:

Cathy and Stephen Graham
Barbara Howard
Dominic Man-Kit Lam
The National Endowment for the Arts
Suzanne and Sanford J. Schlesinger
Betty and Stanley K. Sheinbaum

MARK RUDMAN

Realm of Unknowing

Meditations on Art, Suicide, and Other Transformations

In a new collection of essays, Rudman brings his distinctive sensibility to ruminations on family history, the significance of place, the role of art in clarifying a chaotic world, and the thin, all-too-permeable line between sanity and insanity, restraint and abject cruelty.

"Rudman's voice has such a unique quality, and the spare beauty of his world (as expressed so elegantly and simply) really is the very best kind of poetry . . . I felt humbled. This work is great." —JEANINE BASINGER

"The inquiry, which you follow with brilliance and irony as well as with powerful curiosity, that pushes your writing towards all the recesses of your memory (and your life), is a model of the genre."
—ANTOINE de BAECQUE, *Cahiers du Cinema*

"Mark Rudman's criticism is a unique blend of passion, clarity, and disquiet . . . In challenging himself, Rudman provokes us to challenge ourselves, and the result is a book [*Diverse Voices*] of exceptional quality." —PAUL AUSTER

$35.00 cloth / $14.95 paper

Winner of the National Book Critics Circle Award for Poetry

Rider

"In an elegant, elegiac poem that recovers his relationship with his rabbi stepfather, 'the Jewish Rider,' Rudman has created a formal *tour de force* in which grief, memory and passion are dramatically played out in an elongated question and answer session." —*Publishers Weekly*

"*Rider* is a dynamic, passionate, many-textured dialogue between writer and his ghosts, obsessive, caustic, grieving, and witty, a sort of novel sometimes pitched in verse . . . fully, rewardingly human." —*Harvard Review*

Wesleyan Poetry. $25.00 cloth / $12.95 paper

WESLEYAN UNIVERSITY PRESS

New England

University Press of New England • Hanover, NH 03755-2048 • 800-421-1561

Theater

Looking for exciting new plays and critical debate?

Theater is America's most informative and provocative publication for and about the contemporary stage. Recent issues have included:

Special sections

Brecht Symposium, Sarajevo's War Theater, Queer Theater, Theater and Ecology, South African Theater, and Russian Theater.

Interviews

Susan Sontag, Robbie McCauley, Peter Shumann, Holly Hughes, Elfriede Jelinek, Théâtre du Soleil.

Essays

Harold Bloom, Una Chadhuri, John Clum, Elinor Fuchs, Mark Gevisser, Richard Gilman, Gitta Honegger, Dragan Klaić, Xerxes Mehta, Erika Munk, Peggy Phelan, Marc Robinson, Gordon Rogoff, Denis Salter, and Alisa Solomon.

New Plays

Peter Handke's *The Hour We Knew Nothing of Each Other* • Suzan-Lori Parks' *Imperceptible Mutabilities in the Third Kingdom* • Richard Foreman's *My Head Was a Sledgehammer* • Maria Irene Fornes' *Terra Incognita* • Len Jenkin and John Arnone's *Dr. Divine Presents...* • John Jesurun's *Philoktetes*

AND COMING IN OUR NEXT ISSUE...

❂ UTOPIA ❂

A SPECIAL DOUBLE ISSUE OF UTOPIAN THEATER PROJECTS AND IDEAS TO BE PUBLISHED IN THE SUMMER OF 1995

What would theatrical utopia look like?

Plays, designs, essays, interviews, artwork, and plans from artists and critics including:

Jane Alexander • Rustom Bharucha • Liz Diamond • Erik Ehn • Cheryl Faver • Richard Foreman • Maria Irene Fornes • Guillermo Gomez-Peña • Mel Gordon • Anne Hamburger • David Herskovits • Stanley Kauffmann • Adrienne Kennedy • Dragan Klaić • Tony Kushner • Mark Lord • Judith Malina • Stuart Sherman • Anna Deavere Smith • Alisa Solomon • Mac Wellman • Robert Wilson • and many more!

Theater Order Form

Order your copy of the double issue on theatrical utopias for $12, or subscribe now at the special introductory rate of $18 for the year. Theater *is published three times yearly by the Yale School of Drama and the Yale Repertory Theater.*

Please make checks payable to Theater Magazine, and send order to the magazine at 222 York Street, New Haven, CT 06520.

	Individual		Institution	
○ One year subscription	$~~22~~	$18	$~~35~~	$30
○ Two year subscription	$~~40~~	$34	$~~65~~	$60

Name _____

Address _____

_____

_____

Foreign subscribers: Please add $5.50 a year for postage. A complete list of back issues is available on request.

Total Enclosed: $ _____

Back Issues of Grand Street

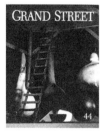

An Indispensable Collection

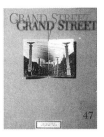

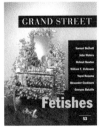

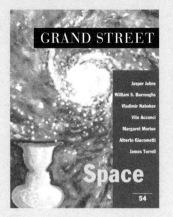

GRAND STREET

Jasper Johns
William S. Burroughs
Vladimir Nabokov
Vito Acconci
Margaret Morton
Alberto Giacometti
James Turrell

Space

54

Some of the bookstores where

GRAND STREET

can be found :

Black Oak Books, Berkeley, CA
Bookstore Fiona, Carson, CA
University of California Books, Irvine, CA
Museum of Contemporary Art, Los Angeles, CA
Diesel Books, Oakland, CA
Logos, Santa Cruz, CA
Arcana, Santa Monica, CA
Small World Books, Venice, CA
Stone Lion Books, Fort Collins, CO
Yale Co-op, New Haven, CT
University of Connecticut Bookstore, Storrs, CT
Bookworks, Washington, DC
Oxford Bookstore, Atlanta, GA
Iowa Book & Supply, Iowa City, IA
Prairie Lights, Iowa City, IA
University Books, Iowa City, IA
Seminary Co-op, Chicago, IL
Von's Book Shop, West Lafayette, IN
Carmichael's, Louisville, KY
Waterstone's Books, Boston, MA
M.I.T. Press Bookstore, Cambridge, MA
Nantucket Books, Nantucket, MA
Broadside Books, Northampton, MA
Provincetown Books, Provincetown, MA
Books Etc., Portland, ME
Book Beat, Oak Park, MI
Baxter's Books, Minneapolis, MN
Walker Art Center Books, Minneapolis, MN

Hungry Mind Bookstore, St. Paul, MN
Whistler's, Kansas City, MO
Left Bank Books, St. Louis, MO
Nebraska Bookstore, Lincoln, NE
Dartmouth Books, Hanover, NH
Micawber Books, Princeton, NJ
Salt of the Earth, Albuquerque, NM
Collected Works, Santa Fe, NM
Community Books, Brooklyn, NY
Talking Leaves, Buffalo, NY
Book Revue, Huntington, NY
The Bookery, Ithaca, NY
Doubleday Books, New York, NY
Gotham Book Mart, New York, NY
St. Mark's Bookstore, New York, NY
Wendell's Books, New York, NY
UC Bookstore, Cincinnati, OH
Books & Co., Dayton, OH
Looking Glass Books, Portland, OR
Farley's Bookshop, New Hope, PA
Bradd Alan Books, Philadelphia, PA
Joseph Fox Books, Philadelphia, PA
College Hill, Providence, RI
Chapter Two Books, Charleston, SC
Open Book, Greenville, SC
Xanadu Bookstore, Memphis, TN
DiverseBooks, Houston, TX
Sam Weller's, Salt Lake City, UT
Williams Corner, Charlottesville, VA
Studio Art Shop, Charlottesville, VA
Northshire Books, Manchester, VT
Woodland Patter, Milwaukee, WI